P9-EGL-660
First Edition

triumphlearning™
Common Core Coach
English Language Arts 7
Assessments

Common Core Coach Assessments, English Language Arts, First Edition, Grade 7
T106NAA

ISBN-13: 978-1-61997-458-6

Cover Design: Q2A/Bill Smith
Cover Illustration: Paul Garland

Triumph Learning® 136 Madison Avenue, 7th Floor, New York, NY 10016

© 2013 Triumph Learning, LLC
Buckle Down and Coach are imprints of Triumph Learning

All rights reserved. No part of this publication may be reproduced in whole or in part, stored
in a retrieval system, or transmitted in any form or by any means, electronic, mechanical,
photocopying, recording or otherwise, without written permission from the publisher.

Printed in the United States of America.

10 9 8 7 6 5 4 3 2 1

The National Governors Association Center for Best Practices and Council of Chief State School Officers
are the sole owners and developers of the Common Core State Standards, © Copyright 2010. All rights reserved.

Contents

Duplicating any part of this book is prohibited by law.

Benchmark Assessment

Duplicating any part of this book is prohibited by law.

Part 1: Reading Comprehension

Read the passage and answer the questions that follow.

Jing's Fantastic Dream

Long ago, in a village near the Huang He River, a young woman named Jing lived a hard and lonely life.

She had been orphaned as a baby. Both of her parents were lost in a flood after the waters of the Huang He surged through their hut. Jing, however, survived. The swollen river carried her off, asleep in her basket, and left her on the edge of a rice field. As it happened, an old peasant woman soon passed through the field on her way to the village, and she heard the baby crying.

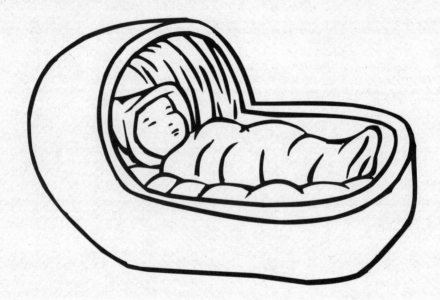

"This child must be blessed," the old woman whispered to herself when she saw the tiny infant in such an unlikely place. "South is the luckiest direction, and the baby's basket has landed on the southernmost tip of this rice field."

Immediately, the old woman carried the basket to the comfortable house of Shan, who produced silk thread in her barn. "Take care of this child," she told Shan, "and she will bring good fortune to your home some day."

Shan nodded and agreed to the request because the old woman was known far and wide for her wisdom.

In time, Jing grew into a bright, young woman, but she was humble and shy. Shan fed Jing and gave her a corner to sleep in. In return for the food and <u>stingy lodging</u>, Jing cared for Shan's six children. Another one of her jobs was to wash waste from the cocoons of silkworms after workers had peeled the silk threads from them. She rinsed the cocoons in a vat and poured the contents of the vat into a tub. A mat prevented the cocoons from going down the drain with the water, and Shan would use them later for stuffing quilts.

Duplicating any part of this book is prohibited by law.

One day, Jing removed the cocoons from the tub and lifted the leftover lint that had collected on top of the mat. She discovered that the wet fuzz on the mat had dried into a thick, crisp sheet. Jing put the sheet of lint to the side, thinking that she would collect more and use the lint sheets to make little hats for the dolls of Shan's children.

Some time later, messengers arrived to announce that the emperor's wife had given birth to a boy—his first son and heir. In one week, there would be a parade, during which his subjects could present gifts to commemorate the great event.

Members of Shan's household jabbered excitedly about their planned gifts. They all understood that the gift-giving would provide a chance to impress the emperor. Even Shan's children were getting presents ready for the emperor's new heir. But poor Jing had nothing for the baby: no rice cakes, no cookies, no tea, no jade, and no silk.

That night, while Jing slept, the old woman appeared in her dream. She smiled, waving a blue sheet, and whispered: "Do not be miserable or uncertain, Jing. All will turn out well. Trust your imagination to solve your problem."

When Jing awoke, she understood the old woman's message. Jing took out the small sheets of lint that she had saved during the year. She pressed them together into a long, wide sheet. Next, she crushed some berries into a paste and dabbed the paste onto the sheet to create floral designs. Now, Jing's gift was complete—a baby blanket that she could offer proudly to the emperor's heir.

Jing soon forgot about the gift after she had presented it to the emperor's son. Then one day, a messenger sent by the emperor appeared at Shan's door, looking for Jing. He bowed to the young woman, placed a sack at her feet, and said, "The emperor sends this gold as thanks for your wondrous gift to his heir. He also requests that you come to the royal palace and use your knowledge to produce more of those remarkable sheets."

And so, Jing left the small village behind to develop her art at the royal palace. At first, her sheets were used for items such as clothing and blankets. In time, though, the Chinese found they could use smoother sheets for writing. Thus, it is said that an orphan named Jing created the first paper in ancient China.

Duplicating any part of this book is prohibited by law.

1. Why was the baby Jing supposed to bring good fortune?

   A. She was an orphan.

   B. She survived a flood.

   C. She was found in a lucky place.

   D. She was saved by a wise woman.

2. Read these sentences from the passage.

   Shan fed Jing and gave her a corner to sleep in. In return for the food and <u>stingy lodging</u>, Jing cared for Shan's six children.

   Which is the BEST definition of <u>stingy lodging</u>?

   A. poor shelter

   B. impossible situation

   C. temporary place to stay

   D. narrow bed

3. Based on Shan's actions in the passage, you can conclude that she is

   A. cruel.

   B. greedy.

   C. practical.

   D. generous.

4. Which detail shows that Jing cares for others?

   A. She helps Shan with the silkworm cocoons.

   B. She plans to make hats for Shan's children's dolls.

   C. She does not have anything to give to the emperor's baby.

   D. She pays attention to her dream about the old woman.

Duplicating any part of this book is prohibited by law.

5. Which of Jing's characteristics BEST explains why she earns the attention of the emperor?

   A. She is lucky.

   B. She is humble.

   C. She is shy.

   D. She uses her imagination.

6. What is the theme of this passage? Give an example from the passage that shows this theme.

   _____

   _____

   _____

   _____

   _____

Duplicating any part of this book is prohibited by law.

The Arbor Day Plan

From the moment I became a student at West Park Middle School, I loved the tall sweet gum tree that shaded one corner of the lawn behind the school. I had never seen anything like it before. It had star-shaped leaves! And that October, those leaves changed into every possible color of autumn—from yellow to purple.

I guess it might be strange for a seventh-grader like me to make a big deal about a tree. But to me, this tree was like magic. It was my special place, my Eden. You see, I was new to town. I didn't know anyone. At lunchtime, we could eat outside, and I would just wander over to that tree and enjoy my lunch in its shade. After a few days, a few other kids joined me there. And that was how I met and made my first and closest friends at West Park Middle School: under the starry leaves of the sweet gum tree.

That was months ago; neither the sweet gum tree nor any other tree has leaves right now. But I have trees on my mind, and I'm making a plan.

It all started when I saw an article in the newspaper saying that the mayor was offering grants to people and institutions that were interested in planting trees on Arbor Day, the last Friday in April. The article said that the mayor was interested not only in having the city look prettier, but also in the other benefits that trees bring, such as cleaning the air and cooling the sidewalks and streets. By the time I finished reading the article, I just knew that I wanted our school to get one of those grants. I even dreamed about it that night! In the dream, about a dozen new trees lined the sidewalk in front of school.

In the next morning's newspaper, though, I saw an angry letter to the editor about the mayor's Arbor Day plan. Apparently, the sweet gum tree was the only surviving tree out of the half dozen that students at West Park Middle School had planted about ten years earlier to <u>observe</u> Arbor Day. Other trees that were planted that year died, too. The angry letter writer believed the mayor's money was going to be wasted.

I didn't care. I knew I just had to figure out how to persuade the principal and the mayor that the same thing would not happen again. I decided to start by talking to my science teacher, Ms. Brody.

That Friday, after classes, I poked my head into Ms. Brody's classroom.

"Excuse me, Ms. Brody?" I said. "Do you know anything about planting trees?"

Ms. Brody looked up from her desk, where she was packing up her bag. "Hi, Ginevra. I know a little bit about trees. How can I help you?"

"I think that we should try to get one of those grants from the mayor to plant more trees at the school, maybe along the sidewalk in front of the school. It looks so bare right now. But if we're going to persuade the principal and the mayor to have more trees planted, we have to show that most of the trees won't die this time."

Duplicating any part of this book is prohibited by law.

"That was such a shame," said Ms. Brody. "None of them but the sweet gum made it."

"I *love* that tree!" I said. And then I blushed. I don't think I had ever said so much about myself to a teacher before.

Ms. Brody smiled. "It is a beautiful tree, especially in the fall. OK, I can help out, but I have a couple questions for you. Are you willing to do some research? And do you have friends who can help you out?"

I hadn't asked my friends, but I nodded anyway. I was sure that they would help.

"I think that the problem last time was that some of the trees were not planted correctly. Over the weekend, why don't you see what you can find out about planting and caring for trees? Let me know what you find out on Monday. And bring your friends! We can go from there."

And so my plan began …

Duplicating any part of this book is prohibited by law.

7. Which word BEST describes Ginevra?

   A. shy

   B. dreamy

   C. determined

   D. embarrassed

8. Why does Ginevra call the sweet gum tree her Eden?

   A. because it gives shade

   B. because it has star-shaped leaves

   C. because it is a perfect place to her

   D. because people gather under its branches

9. Read this sentence from the passage.

   Apparently, the sweet gum tree was the only surviving tree out of the half dozen that students at West Park Middle School had planted about ten years earlier to <u>observe</u> Arbor Day.

   Which of the following words that could replace <u>observe</u> in this sentence has a more positive connotation?

   A. notice

   B. remember

   C. mark

   D. celebrate

10. Why does Ginevra think that it might be challenging to persuade the principal to have more trees planted at the school?

   A. The school already has enough trees.

   B. Trees that were planted earlier at the school died.

   C. There is nowhere to plant the trees.

   D. The principal thinks that trees are a waste of money.

Duplicating any part of this book is prohibited by law.

11. Which BEST explains how the point of view in "The Arbor Day Plan" differs from that in "Jing's Fantastic Dream"?

    A. We hear about Ginevra's thoughts directly from her.

    B. We see Ginevra's actions more clearly than Jing's.

    C. We learn more about Ginevra's past than about Jing's.

    D. We understand Ginevra's conflict better than Jing's.

12. Read these sentences from the passage.

> **"I *love* that tree!" I said. And then I blushed. I don't think I had ever said so much about myself to a teacher before.**

What do these sentences reveal about Ginevra's character?

_____

_____

_____

_____

Duplicating any part of this book is prohibited by law.

The Myth of Tantalus

From the time he was a child, few people liked Tantalus. He had only himself to blame, for he was arrogant, bragging day and night about his parentage.

To his mother and his various nannies (none of whom stayed to care for him very long), he would say, "Why should I have to say 'please' and 'thank you'? After all, I am not like other mortals! I am the son of Zeus, the king of the gods!"

To his various tutors (none of whom stayed to teach him for very long), he would say, "Why should I have to learn geography? Or multiplication? Or anything else? After all, I am not like other mortals! I am the son of Zeus, the king of the gods!"

To the other children who invited him to join in their games (none of whom invited him more than once), he would say, "Why should I take part in your silly games? After all, I am not like other mortals! I am the son of Zeus, the king of the gods!"

Needless to say, Tantalus did not change much as he grew into young adulthood. Perhaps he bragged less than he did as a child, and perhaps he was quite handsome and occasionally even charming; nevertheless, he still held himself <u>aloof</u> from others. He had many admirers, but not a single friend.

Tantalus, however, did not care that he had no friends, for he alone of all mortals was regularly invited to dine with the gods on Mount Olympus. *Why should I care for the company of other mortals*, he thought, *if I could enjoy the company of the gods?* And enjoy their company he did, basking in their unearthly glow as he tasted the delights of ambrosia and nectar, food and drink of the gods. Also, his father Zeus sometimes asked Tantalus to sit at his side. With an amused look in his strange, flashing eyes, Zeus listened to the tales that Tantalus told of his life among mortals. However, Hera, the queen of the gods, scorned Tantalus outright; and Apollo, Artemis, Athena, Hermes, and the rest of the gods rarely said a word to the young man at their table.

The ancient poets are silent on why Tantalus alone was honored in this way. They are silent, too, on why Tantalus later decided to try to deceive the gods. Perhaps he grew tired of sitting in their midst while they more or less ignored him. Perhaps he no longer wished to set himself apart from other people. For whatever the reason, Tantalus stole some nectar and ambrosia and took it from Mount Olympus to share with other mortals at his own table. For one glorious evening, he dined happily among his fellow mortals, and it was as though he had actual friends.

Foolish Tantalus! Did he really think that the gods would not notice? Not a day passed before he was called before the mighty Zeus.

"How dare you steal our food and drink to share with mere mortals!" Zeus roared. "Yours was a rare privilege! This abuse of our trust is unforgivable!"

Then, the flashing eyes of Zeus clouded over. "I am sorry, my son. But now and forevermore, you are condemned to live under the watch of my brother, Hades."

Duplicating any part of this book is prohibited by law.

And, even as Zeus's words resounded through the great hall on Mount Olympus, Tantalus found himself suddenly transported to the underworld and staring into the cold blue eyes of Hades.

"Your punishment is to live in this pool," said Hades, and as he spoke, a pool of water welled up around Tantalus's feet. "But however thirsty you may be, you will never drink of the water of this pool."

Tantalus, bewildered, reached out to cup some water in his hands, but the pool drained into the ground, appearing again only when he stopped reaching for the water.

"Fruit trees may happen to grow by the side of the pool," said Hades, and as he spoke, trees sprang up, blossomed, and let their petals go. Soon their branches were heavy with apples, pears, and pomegranates. "But however hungry you may be," he continued, "you will never eat of their fruit."

Tantalus reached up to grab a pear dangling just above his head, but the wind blew it just out of reach.

And so Tantalus lived, always thirsty, always hungry, in everlasting punishment for his arrogance. And whenever you, too, are *tantalized* to take what is not yours to take, remember the story of Tantalus.

Duplicating any part of this book is prohibited by law.

13. What is MOST LIKELY the reason why the nannies and tutors of Tantalus did not stay to care for or teach him for very long?

A. He intimidated them.

B. He did not listen to them.

C. He did not really need them.

D. He was a violent child.

14. Which tells what <u>aloof</u> means as it is used in this passage?

A. apart

B. entertaining

C. attractive

D. lonely

15. Why did Tantalus MOST LIKELY enjoy the company of the gods on Mount Olympus?

A. Being there confirmed his idea that he was better than other mortals.

B. He enjoyed listening to them tell about their great achievements.

C. They paid attention to his stories about life among mortals.

D. He had never tasted anything better than nectar and ambrosia.

16. Read this sentence from the passage.

For one glorious evening, he dined happily among his fellow mortals, and it was as though he had actual friends.

Based on this sentence, you can conclude that Tantalus

A. shared the nectar and ambrosia to trick his father.

B. wanted to show the gods that people liked him.

C. may have wished that he had friends.

D. had become bored with dining on Mount Olympus.

Duplicating any part of this book is prohibited by law.

17. In what way is Zeus different from his brother Hades?

   A. He has supernatural powers.

   B. He believes that Tantalus should be punished.

   C. He is sorry that Tantalus must be condemned.

   D. He is a good friend to Tantalus.

18. In a summary of 2–3 sentences, explain why Tantalus is punished.

   _____

   _____

   _____

   _____

Duplicating any part of this book is prohibited by law.

Read the passage and answer the questions that follow.

The Recital

If I could live the past month all over again, of course I would do things differently. Who wouldn't? I guess since we can't relive the past, the best we can do is try to do better in the future. In fact, after all the embarrassment I put myself through last night, I hope I'd do better than just *try*. No way would I want to do that to myself again!

Last night was the end-of-year piano recital that my teacher organizes every year. In a way, I guess it's not such a big deal. Maybe your parents come, and maybe your grandparents and brothers and sisters come, too. There aren't any tickets, and people don't come in off the street for the show. It's just a bunch of kids playing the piano, and everybody knows everybody else.

On the other hand, maybe that's the worst part of it. Everyone there knew exactly who I am. If it were just some strangers watching me mess up completely, they would probably forget about it right away.

Yeah, I messed up completely. And I have no one but myself to blame.

My teacher picked a Bach prelude for me to play at the recital. It's a pretty simple piece, but my teacher said it would show off my musicality. She actually said that! She also said, "Your technique needs some improvement, but you have a good ear. If you're serious about the piano, you could go far."

Good ear or not, I really heard only about half of what my teacher said. I heard the parts about my musicality and going far. As for the parts about my technique needing improvement and my needing to be serious, I forgot those until it was much, much too late. Instead of getting serious, I just got arrogant.

During the first week of preparing for the recital, I was supposed to memorize the piece. But I didn't practice enough; and at my next lesson, I had only the first few bars memorized.

Duplicating any part of this book is prohibited by law.

"Tomas," said my teacher, "I cannot have you play in the recital if you don't memorize the music. Playing with the music in front of you—this is just not done!"

During the second week of preparing for the recital, I practiced just enough to memorize the piece. Well, mostly. There was a bit in the middle that I kept messing up. And I could never get the ending quite right. But I figured it would come in time. What was I thinking? I wasn't thinking.

At my next lesson, my teacher was not pleased. "Tomas," she said, "I cannot have you play like this in the recital! This mess in the middle—you should just work on that part an hour each day, if you have to."

An hour each day! I gave it maybe twenty minutes most days, until my next lesson—the last lesson before the recital.

"Tomas," sighed my teacher, "it will have to do."

Looking back, I can't see why I felt so confident about playing at the recital. I actually thought that I would impress everyone! I imagined them complimenting me at the reception after the recital. "Yes, he will go far!" my teacher would say in response to all the praise.

It wasn't until I actually walked on stage that I realized I had made a terrible, terrible mistake by not practicing more. All those eyes looking at me! I broke into a cold sweat. When I sat on the piano bench, my arms were trembling—not good if you're about to play the piano! My fingers stumbled a bit through the first few notes, and I instantly felt even more nervous. My arms shook even more. My fingers stumbled again. I just about lost control of my arms. I couldn't go on—and so I stopped, abruptly, right in the middle of the piece.

Now what? I thought, sitting on the piano bench in silence. What I wanted to do was disappear. Instead, I did the next best thing: I stood up, bowed, and walked off the stage. A few people clapped. They must have been confused.

If I want to go far, I've got to get serious. Arrogance, on the other hand, is clearly going to get me nowhere.

Duplicating any part of this book is prohibited by law.

19. When is Tomas relating the events that occur in this passage?

    A. a long time after the recital

    B. the day after the recital

    C. just before the recital

    D. shortly before his next recital

20. For what reason does Tomas feel confident about performing in the recital?

    A. His teacher said he had talent.

    B. He has practiced regularly.

    C. He has performed well in the past.

    D. He will know everyone in the audience.

21. Based on what she says in the passage, which BEST describes the feelings of Tomas's piano teacher about his preparation for the recital?

    A. confident

    B. disappointed

    C. appreciative

    D. unrealistic

22. Which quotation from the passage shows that Tomas has learned a lesson from his experience in the recital?

    A. "No way would I want to do that to myself again!"

    B. "In a way, I guess it's not such a big deal."

    C. "On the other hand, maybe that's the worst part of it."

    D. "What I wanted to do was disappear."

Duplicating any part of this book is prohibited by law.

23. The themes of "The Myth of Tantalus" and "The Recital" are similar in that they are both about

A. anger.

B. greed.

C. laziness.

D. arrogance.

24. In both the myth about Tantalus and the contemporary passage "The Recital," the main character suffers negative consequences of a major character flaw. How do these consequences differ in the two passages?

_____

_____

_____

_____

_____

Duplicating any part of this book is prohibited by law.

Part 2: Language Arts

This passage contains mistakes. Read the passage and answer the questions that follow.

The Tickets

(1) What a dilemma!

(2) Keenan's parents had gotten tickets to see the first game at the new minor-league baseball park. (3) They had bought four tickets: one each for themselves, one for Keenan, and one so that Keenan could take a friend.

(4) "Great!" said Keenan. (5) "I'll ask Milo if he can come." (6) Milo was Keenan's best friend.

(7) Later that evening, though, Keenan started to <u>wonder</u>. (8) Did Milo even *like* baseball? (9) Keenan wasn't sure. (10) He talked about baseball with Milo all the time, but Milo never showed the kind of enthusiasm about the game that their friend Isaac did. (11) Not only did Isaac play shortstop in a local league, but he and his father went to see several Tigers games every year.

(12) At breakfast the next morning, Keenan told his parents, "I don't know. (13) Maybe I'll ask Isaac to come to the game. (14) He certainly likes baseball more than Milo does."

(15) "You can take whomever you like," said Keenan's mom. (16) "Just remember that the game is on Saturday, so you'll have to decide soon."

(17) On the bus ride to school, Keenan again started to wonder. (18) Would Milo's feelings be hurt if he asked Isaac to the game? (19) Keenan was certainly sure that his friend would understand, but Milo still might feel left out. (20) Isaac might not care so much about going to a minor-league game. (21) After all, he got to see major-league teams play several times each year.

(22) Should he ask Milo to the game? (23) Or should he ask Isaac? (24) By the time he returned home from school, Keenan was beginning to suspect that there was only one way he could possibly come to a solution for his dilemma, and that he could only find that solution by flipping a coin. (25) He didn't particularly care for that solution, though.

(26) He was doing his homework at the kitchen table when his mother got home from work. (27) "I talked to your aunt today, and guess what she told me about your cousin?" she said.

(28) "You mean Jennie?" asked Keenan. (29) "No, what?"

(30) "Her softball team is going to be competing for the state championships. (31) Maybe we can go to one of the games."

(32) "Excellent!" said Keenan. (33) And then an idea struck him. (34) "Hey, why don't we ask Jennie to go to the game with us on Saturday?"

(35) Keenan's mom laughed. (36) "That's a great way to solve your <u>dilemma</u>. (37) Yes, let's ask her!"

Duplicating any part of this book is prohibited by law.

25. Which of the following is a complex sentence?

A. He talked about baseball with Milo all the time, but Milo never showed the kind of enthusiasm about the game that their friend Isaac did.

B. On the bus ride to school, Keenan again started to wonder.

C. Isaac, on the other hand, might not even care so much about going to a minor-league game.

D. He was doing his homework at the kitchen table when his mother got home from work.

26. Read this entry from a dictionary.

> **wonder** (WUHN-duhr) *verb, without an object* **1.** to think with curiosity **2.** to be filled with awe, to marvel (usually followed by *at*) **3.** to doubt *verb, with an object* **4.** to be curious about

Which definition of <u>wonder</u> is used in sentence 7?

A. meaning 1

B. meaning 2

C. meaning 3

D. meaning 4

27. Read sentence 19 from the passage.

> **Keenan was certainly sure that his friend would understand, but Milo still might feel left out.**

Which word in sentence 19 is LEAST necessary and should be deleted?

A. certainly

B. would

C. still

D. out

28. Read sentences 20 and 21 from the passage.

> **Isaac might not care so much about going to a minor-league game. After all, he got to see major-league teams play several times each year.**

Which is the correct way to combine these sentences into one complex sentence?

A. Isaac might not care so much about going to a minor-league game, after all, he got to see major-league teams play several times each year.

B. Isaac might not care so much about going to a minor-league game because he got to see major-league teams play several times each year.

C. After seeing major-league teams play several times each year, Isaac might not care so much about going to a minor-league game.

D. Used to seeing major-league teams play several times each year, Isaac might not care so much about going to a minor-league game.

Duplicating any part of this book is prohibited by law.

29. Read this entry from a thesaurus.

    dilemma   crisis, embarrassment, mess, problem

Which word is the BEST to use in place of <u>dilemma</u> in sentence 36?

A. crisis

B. embarrassment

C. mess

D. problem

30. Read sentence 24 from the passage.

By the time he returned home from school, Keenan was beginning to suspect that there was only one way he could possibly come to a solution for his dilemma, and that he could only find that solution by flipping a coin.

Rewrite this sentence so that it is less wordy and its meaning is clearer.

_____

_____

_____

_____

_____

Duplicating any part of this book is prohibited by law.

Part 3: Writing

Read the passage and respond to the prompt that follows.

The Three Questions

adapted from a story by Leo Tolstoy

Once upon a time, a king announced that he would give a great reward to anyone who would teach him what was the right time for every action, and who were the most important people, and how he might know what was the most important activity for him to do.

Learned men came to the king, but they all answered his questions differently, so he gave the reward to none. But still wishing to find the answers to his questions, he decided to consult a hermit, widely renowned for his wisdom.

The hermit lived in a forest and welcomed no visitors except common folk. So the king put on simple clothes and, before reaching the hermit's hut, left his horse and bodyguards behind.

The hermit was digging up the ground in front of his hut. Seeing the king, he greeted him and went on digging. Frail and weak, the hermit breathed heavily at the work.

The king went up to him and said: "I have come to you, wise hermit, to ask you to answer three questions: How can I learn to do the right thing at the right time? Who are the people I most need? And what activity is the most important for me to do?"

The hermit listened to the king, but answered nothing. He just spat on his hand and continued digging.

"You are tired," said the king, "let me take the spade and work awhile for you."

"Thanks!" said the hermit, and, giving the spade to the king, he sat down on the ground.

One hour passed, and another. The sun began to sink behind the trees, and the king at last stuck the spade into the ground, and said, "I came to you, wise man, for an answer to my questions. If you can give me none, tell me so, and I will return home."

"Here comes someone running," said the hermit. "Let us see who it is."

The king turned around and saw a bearded man running out of the forest toward him. When he reached the king, he fell fainting on the ground, moaning feebly. The king and the hermit unfastened the man's clothing. There was a large wound in his stomach. The king washed it as best he could and bandaged it with his handkerchief and with a towel that the hermit had. When at last the blood ceased flowing, the man revived and asked for something to drink. The king brought fresh water and gave it to him.

Meanwhile, the sun had set, and it had become cool. So the king, with the hermit's help, carried the wounded man into the hut and laid him on the bed. Lying on the bed, the man closed his eyes and was quiet; but the king was so tired from his walk and from the work he had done, that he crouched down on the threshold and also fell asleep. When he awoke in the morning, it was a long time before he could remember where he was or who was the strange bearded man lying on the bed and gazing intently at him with shining eyes.

Duplicating any part of this book is prohibited by law.

"Forgive me!" said the bearded man in a weak voice.

"I do not know you and have nothing to forgive you for," said the king.

"You do not know me, but I know you. Long ago, I swore to revenge myself on you because you seized my property. I knew you had gone alone to see the hermit, and I resolved to kill you on your way back. But the day passed, and you did not return. So I went out to find you and came upon your bodyguards, and they recognized and wounded me. I escaped from them but would have bled to death if you had not dressed my wound. I wanted to kill you, and you have saved my life. Forgive me!"

The king was very glad to have made peace. He not only forgave his enemy but also said that he would send his servants and his own physician to take care of the wounded man and promised to restore his property.

The king then went out onto the porch and looked around for the hermit. The king saw him, approached him, and said, "For the last time, I beg you to answer my questions, wise man."

"You have already been answered!" said the hermit.

"How am I answered? What do you mean?"

"Do you not see? If you had not pitied my weakness yesterday and had not dug those beds for me and had gone your way, that man would have attacked you. So the most important time was when you were digging the beds, and I was the most important person, and to do me good was your most important business. Afterward, when that man ran to us, the most important time was when you were attending to him, for if you had not bound up his wounds, he would have died without having made peace with you. So he was the most important person, and what you did for him was your most important business.

"Remember then: There is only one time that is important—Now! It is the only time when we have any power. The most important persons are the ones with whom you are. And the most important activity for you is to do good for them!"

Duplicating any part of this book is prohibited by law.

Response to Literature Prompt

Describe the king in "The Three Questions." Based on his actions, his words, and the words of others, explain why the king is able to learn the hermit's lesson.

Use the checklist below to help you do your best writing.

Does your response to literature

❏ introduce a claim?

❏ support the claim with logical reasoning and relevant, accurate evidence from the text?

❏ organize reasons and evidence in a logical structure?

❏ use transitional words and phrases to help readers follow your argument?

❏ use a formal style and vocabulary suitable for the audience and purpose?

❏ have a conclusion that supports your argument?

❏ use correct spelling and use conventional grammar and mechanics?

Use the following pages to plan and write your response.

Duplicating any part of this book is prohibited by law.

Planning Page

Duplicating any part of this book is prohibited by law.

Duplicating any part of this book is prohibited by law.

Duplicating any part of this book is prohibited by law.

Duplicating any part of this book is prohibited by law.

Duplicating any part of this book is prohibited by law.

Benchmark Assessment 2

Duplicating any part of this book is prohibited by law.

Part 1: Reading Comprehension

Read the passage and answer the questions that follow.

The Business Trip That Took Twenty-Four Years

A Family of Traders

Although it often took several years to travel between European countries and the Far East in the 1200s, traders such as Niccoló Polo and his brother Maffeo were willing to take these long journeys because they were so profitable. People in the Polos' home city of Venice, the powerful city-state that became part of present-day Italy, were willing to pay high prices for things brought back from faraway countries in Asia. As a result, the Polos soon became wealthy merchants. Their family crest appeared above warehouses and places of business as far away as Constantinople and various cities on the Black Sea.

When Niccoló and Maffeo made their first trip to China (which Europeans then called *Cathay*), Niccoló's son Marco was so young that he had to stay behind in Venice with his mother. By the time he was seventeen years old, however, Marco was ready to accompany his father and his uncle as they set out on a second trip to the Far East. The purpose of this journey was, as always, simple: to find people to trade with and goods to bring back to Venice.

A Changing World

The Polos' journey was possible, in part, because of events that had taken place in the early 1200s. A great warrior named Genghis Khan had united tribes in central Asia and established the Mongol Empire. It became the largest continuous-land empire that the world has ever seen. It extended from the Pacific Ocean to the eastern edge of Europe and the Middle East, north to the Arctic, and south to the Indian Ocean.

The Mongols favored trade. They reopened the trading route between Europe and Asia, which is known as the Silk Road and which had been blocked for many years because of war. The Polos were among the first Europeans to take advantage of the opportunities for trade created by the Mongols. Their 7,500-mile journey to China took nearly four years. They traveled mainly overland to the court of the Kublai Khan, who was the grandson of Genghis Khan and his successor as ruler of the Mongol Empire.

A Remarkable Adventure

Marco, Niccoló, and Maffeo Polo remained in China as Kublai Khan's guests for seventeen years. During that time, they witnessed sights that few Europeans had even imagined. The Polos were surprised by the use of paper money rather than gold or silver. They marveled that citizens wore silk garments and ate from porcelain bowls.

On the return trip, the Polos traveled around Indochina and along the coast of India before heading overland back to Venice. They reached home in 1295—twenty-four years after they had started out!

Duplicating any part of this book is prohibited by law.

A Priceless Book

When the Polos arrived in their homeland, Venice was at war with Genoa, another city-state that became part of present-day Italy. In this war, Marco was captured and put in prison. While he was in prison, Marco dictated his stories about his travels to another prisoner, who was a popular writer. The writer recorded Marco's account in a book called *Description of the World*, which we know as *The Travels of Marco Polo*.

The book was widely read in Europe. It introduced readers to the wonders of places they did not know existed. Marco's descriptions of exotic customs and precious objects, however, caused some people to doubt his stories. They began to call Marco's book "The Million Lies."

In spite of such criticisms, Marco Polo's book had a great influence. His system for measuring distances was so remarkably accurate that two hundred years after his death, mapmakers still relied on his descriptions of central Asia. Furthermore, his book inspired explorers in the 1400s and 1500s to sail east to see Japan and the other places that Marco Polo had been the first European to describe. Christopher Columbus even used the book to estimate how long it would take him to sail west around the world to Asia.

At the end of their twenty-four-year business trip, the Polos returned to Europe with many valuable goods for trade, such as silk, jewels, spices, and perfumes. Although they did not realize it at the time, the most valuable thing that the Polos brought back was Marco's amazingly detailed account of their journey. His book opened up the world by inspiring people to travel and make their own connections with distant lands.

Duplicating any part of this book is prohibited by law.

1. Which text structure is used in this passage?

   A. cause and effect

   B. problem and solution

   C. compare and contrast

   D. chronological order

2. Which BEST explains why the Polos were able to become wealthy?

   A. They made more than one trip to the Far East.

   B. They lived in a powerful city-state on the Italian peninsula.

   C. They owned warehouses and places of business in distant cities.

   D. They were willing to travel far for goods that people in Venice paid a lot of money to buy.

3. Why is the second section of the passage titled "A Changing World"?

   A. It tells about the effects of Europe on the Polos' travels.

   B. It tells how Genghis Khan conquered the peoples of Asia.

   C. It tells how the Mongols' rule transformed trade between Asia and Europe.

   D. It tells that Kublai Khan inherited the Mongol Empire from his grandfather.

4. What can you infer from the sights that surprised the Polos in Asia?

   A. Paper money was not used in Europe at the time.

   B. Europeans were disgusted by materials such as silk and porcelain.

   C. There was no gold or silver to be found in China.

   D. The Polos were homesick during their years with Kublai Khan.

Duplicating any part of this book is prohibited by law.

5. Which sentence from the passage BEST supports the idea that some people trusted the information in Marco Polo's book?

   A. "While he was in prison, Marco dictated his stories about his travels to another prisoner, who was a popular writer."

   B. "The book was widely read in Europe."

   C. "Christopher Columbus even used the book to estimate how long it would take him to sail west around the world to Asia."

   D. "His book opened up the world by inspiring people to travel and make their own connections with distant lands."

6. Based on information in the passage, explain whether or not the author of the passage supports the viewpoint that Marco Polo's book was one of lies.

   _____

   _____

   _____

   _____

Duplicating any part of this book is prohibited by law.

On the Way to Cathay:
from the Journal of Carlo Fremonte

1271

We have just set sail from Venice, and I have never been more excited—or terrified! Before today, I had never been more than a mile outside of my city. But today, I, Carlo Fremonte, am starting off on a journey to Cathay!

As the third son of a goldsmith, there is no place for me in my father's business. I could hardly believe my good fortune when Marco Polo asked me to accompany him, his uncle Maffeo, and his father, Niccoló, and tend to their needs during this journey. Marco is seventeen, just four years older than me, and his family is very famous in Venice.

Late 1271

I remember very little of our voyage across the Mediterranean from Venice to Acre in the Holy Land because I was so seasick on that awful ship. The overland passage we've been on since leaving Acre is difficult and dangerous, but I am learning about things I never could have imagined. I try to record every experience in my journal, but Marco keeps far more detailed accounts.

Marco has a very good eye for details, and his knowledge of languages is amazing. He can speak and write Tartar, along with Persian and other languages. He records everything in small notebooks that he reviews often.

1272

Much time has passed since I left my home. Marco became ill, and we stopped for nearly a year while he recovered. We were only halfway to Cathay at the time. We were near the Pamir Mountains, which surely must be the highest place in the world!

Of all the perils we have experienced so far, none compares with the one we now face. We are about to cross the Gobi Desert. It will take us a month to travel across the desert at its narrowest place. Today, we met a caravan of wagons traveling in the opposite direction. The leader advised us to stay close together. "If you fall behind or become separated from your party in the Gobi Desert," he warned, "you are in great danger. You can easily get lost and will likely never be seen or heard from again!"

1273

Oddly, the desert is more bare rock than sand. There is nothing at all to eat. At night, we can hear the wind howling all around us. Before sleeping, we must tie bells to all of our animals and set a sign in the ground, pointing the way to go in the morning. Otherwise, we might easily forget which direction to travel. I feel even more afraid in the Gobi Desert than I did on that <u>accursed</u> ship in the Mediterranean.

Duplicating any part of this book is prohibited by law.

Niccoló and Maffeo estimate that we are still forty days away from the Great Khan's court in the great city of Xanadu. The Mongol ruler must be aware of our approach, however, because his guide has come to meet us and give us safe passage to the palace.

1274

After nearly four years, we have reached our destination! The palace of the Great Khan is more luxurious than anything I have ever dreamed of. It is made of marble, and its glittering green roof can be seen for miles. Its walls are covered with gold and silver, and the hall is large enough for 6,000 dinner guests.

I am continually amazed at the wonders of the Far East. Will anyone in Europe believe that the Mongols burn black rocks to heat their rooms? Will anyone believe that sheets of paper are used for money? I doubt it.

1275

We are treated like royalty here. Marco is a favorite of the Great Khan, who asks him often to tell stories of the lands through which we passed.

I do not know what Marco plans to do or how long he will stay here. But I know this: I will remain here, whatever the Polos decide to do. The Great Khan prefers to employ foreigners as officers in his government, so there is work for me here. I intend to stay.

Duplicating any part of this book is prohibited by law.

7. Which BEST explains the meaning of <u>accursed</u> as it is used in this passage?

   A. spellbinding

   B. sought after

   C. likely to sink

   D. greatly disliked

8. How does Carlo's reaction to the palace of Kublai Khan compare with his reactions to the Mediterranean Sea and to the Gobi Desert?

   A. He finds all of them exotic and terrifying.

   B. He cannot wait to leave them and return to Europe.

   C. He marvels at the palace but is glad to leave the sea and the desert.

   D. He enjoys adventure but does not know how to behave in a palace.

9. Which word BEST describes Carlo at the end of the passage?

   A. homesick

   B. ambitious

   C. dreamy

   D. wealthy

10. Based on Carlo's descriptions of him, you can BEST characterize Marco Polo as

   A. observant.

   B. boring.

   C. attention-seeking.

   D. frail.

Duplicating any part of this book is prohibited by law.

11. What detail from the passage MOST LIKELY explains why the Polos stayed in China so long?

    A. The journey to China took four years.

    B. Kublai Khan's palace was luxurious.

    C. Marco Polo was asked to tell stories about his travels.

    D. Kublai Khan preferred to employ foreigners.

12. What does the viewpoint of the fictional character of Carlo Fremonte give to the story of the Polos that a nonfiction account, such as "The Business Trip That Took Twenty-Four Years," does not have?

_____

_____

_____

_____

Duplicating any part of this book is prohibited by law.

The Indian Removal Act and the Trail of Tears

When white settlers from Europe first arrived in America, many of them tended to look at Native Americans as uncivilized savages. Because of this viewpoint, settlers felt justified in breaking treaties and taking land from Native Americans. In the late 1820s, gold was found on Cherokee land in the state of Georgia. The results were disastrous for all Native American tribes who lived east of the Mississippi River.

Sequoyah

The Cherokee

Through a series of twenty-eight treaties made between 1684 and 1819, the Cherokee lost about 90 percent of their ancestral lands to white settlers. By the 1800s, the Cherokee had begun to absorb some of the culture of white settlers. For this reason, the Cherokee were known as one of the Five Civilized Tribes of the Southeast. They lived in houses, grew crops, raised livestock, and attended schools. Some Cherokee operated businesses, such as blacksmith shops, sawmills, and stores.

In 1821, a Cherokee named Sequoyah invented a writing system for the Cherokee language. The speed at which the Cherokee became literate was amazing. By 1828, they were publishing their own weekly newspaper, called *The Cherokee Phoenix*. The tribe also wrote a constitution and developed a system of government similar to that of the United States.

The Indian Removal Act

In creating their own constitution, the Cherokee declared themselves an independent republic. The state of Georgia did not look kindly on this declaration. After the 1828 discovery of gold on Cherokee land, the state passed a law taking away the legal authority of the Cherokee over their own land.

Duplicating any part of this book is prohibited by law.

Georgia found a friend in Andrew Jackson, who became president in 1829 and held the office through early 1837. In 1812–1813, Jackson had fought side-by-side with the Cherokee in the Creek War. Nevertheless, he saw all Native Americans as inferior to whites and believed that their culture was bound to fade away. In 1830, he persuaded Congress to pass the Indian Removal Act. This law gave the president the right to grant land west of the Mississippi River to Native American tribes living within any of the states. (At that time, nearly all of the states were east of the Mississippi.) In exchange for this western land, the Native Americans were to give up their land in the east.

Conflict Between Cherokee Leaders

The leaders of the Cherokee did not agree about how to respond to the Indian Removal Act. Most Cherokee supported Principal Chief John Ross in working against removal. Ross worked to rally support among whites who favored Native American rights, as well as among President Jackson's political opponents in Washington, D.C.

Other leaders, such as Major Ridge, believed that the Cherokee had no choice but to accept relocation. With a very small group of Cherokee, he negotiated and signed the Treaty of New Echota with the U.S. government in 1835. The majority of Cherokee rejected this treaty, but this fact did not stop the federal government from forcing all of them from their land.

The Trail of Tears

Imagine soldiers with guns entering your home and forcing you to leave. They give you no time to gather your belongings or even pack food, clothing, and blankets necessary for survival. This is what happened to the Cherokee in 1838 when the U.S. military began to force them from their homes.

Within twenty-five days, as many as 15,000 Cherokee were taken to military prisons called stockades. Food and water were in short supply, and sanitation was poor. Many people became ill and died. Many of the so-called doctors assigned to each camp had no real medical training and did little to help the sick.

Through the fall and winter of 1838–1839, the Cherokee were sent west in groups of about a thousand. Food, shelter, and clothing were inadequate. U.S. troops refused to stop to allow people to rest. As many as four thousand Cherokee died. The route to their new home in what is now Oklahoma became known as the "Trail of Tears."

Timeline of the Indian Removal Act

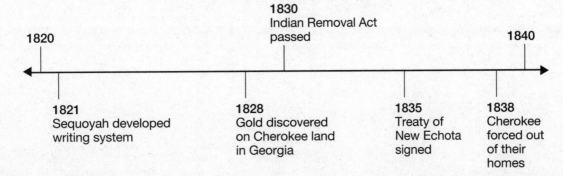

Duplicating any part of this book is prohibited by law.

Although President Jackson could propose a law such as the Indian Removal Act, only Congress can make new laws. How does it do so?

- One or more legislators in either chamber of Congress (i.e., the Senate or the House of Representatives) introduce(s) a bill, which is a proposal for a new law.
- At least one committee of legislators from that chamber reviews the bill, debates its merits, and then votes on the bill.
- If a majority of committee members vote for the bill, it is passed on to that entire chamber.
- The members of that chamber discuss, debate, and vote on the bill.
- If the bill is approved, it is sent to the other chamber of Congress, where it is introduced (i.e., proposed), goes through committee(s), is discussed and debated, and voted on.
- If the second chamber approves the bill without changing it, then it is sent to the president. (See the last two steps below.)
- If the second chamber changes the bill, then a conference committee, which includes legislators from both chambers, tries to work out the differences between the two versions of the bill and reports on the results.
- If the conference committee agrees on a revised bill, it is sent to both chambers to be discussed, debated, and voted on.
- If both chambers vote to approve the revised bill, it is sent to the president.
- If the president signs the bill, it becomes a law.
- If the president rejects, or vetoes, the bill, it can still become a law if two-thirds of the members of both the Senate and the House of Representatives vote to override the veto.

Duplicating any part of this book is prohibited by law.

13. Which statement from the passage is an opinion?

 A. "Because of this viewpoint, settlers felt justified in breaking treaties and taking land from Native Americans."

 B. "For this reason, the Cherokee were known as one of the Five Civilized Tribes of the Southeast."

 C. "The speed at which the Cherokee became literate was amazing."

 D. "The state of Georgia did not look kindly on this declaration."

14. Which BEST explains the meaning of <u>republic</u> as it is used in this passage?

 A. any independent nation

 B. a nation declaring war on another nation

 C. a state in which citizens hold power

 D. a group trying to break away from a government

15. What was the direct result of the Treaty of New Echota?

 A. Principal Chief John Ross lost the support of most Cherokee.

 B. The U.S. government felt justified in forcing the Cherokee from their homes.

 C. The Cherokee were given no time to prepare for their long trip to the West.

 D. U.S. troops refused to allow Native Americans to rest on the Trail of Tears.

16. What always happens before all senators and all representatives can vote on a bill?

 A. The president decides whether or not to sign it.

 B. A committee representing both chambers reports on the bill.

 C. A committee of legislators reviews, debates, and votes on the bill.

 D. Legislators in the other chamber of Congress debate the bill.

Duplicating any part of this book is prohibited by law.

17. Which of the following events occurred while Andrew Jackson was president?

   A. Sequoyah developed his writing system.

   B. The Treaty of New Echota was signed.

   C. Gold was discovered on Cherokee land in Georgia.

   D. The Cherokee were forced out of their homes.

18. For what reasons did so many Cherokee die between leaving their homes in the East and arriving at their new home in the West? Give at least two reasons from the passage.

   _____

   _____

   _____

   _____

   _____

Duplicating any part of this book is prohibited by law.

Read the speech and answer the questions that follow.

excerpted from the

First Annual Message to Congress
of President Andrew Jackson
December 8, 1829

The ... destiny of the Indian tribes within the limits of some of our States have become objects of much interest and importance. It has long been the policy of Government to introduce among them the arts of civilization, in the hope of gradually reclaiming them from a wandering life. This policy has, however, been coupled with another wholly incompatible with its success. Professing a desire to civilize and settle them, we have at the same time lost no opportunity to purchase their lands and thrust them farther into the wilderness. By this means they have not only been kept in a wandering state, but been led to look upon us as unjust and indifferent to their fate. Thus, though lavish in its expenditures upon the subject, Government has constantly defeated its own policy, and the Indians in general, receding farther and farther to the west, have retained their savage habits. A portion, however, of the Southern tribes, having mingled much with the whites and made some progress in the arts of civilized life, have lately attempted to erect an independent government within the limits of Georgia and Alabama. These States, claiming to be the only <u>sovereigns</u> within their territories, extended their laws over the Indians, which induced the latter to call upon the United States for protection.

There is no constitutional, conventional, or legal provision which allows [the people of Georgia] less power over the Indians within their borders than is possessed by Maine or New York. Would the people of Maine permit the Penobscot tribe to erect an independent government within their State? And unless they did would it not be the duty of the General Government to support them in resisting such a measure? Would the people of New York permit each remnant of the six Nations within her borders to declare itself an independent people under the protection of the United States? Could the Indians establish a separate republic on each of their reservations in Ohio? And if they were so disposed would it be the duty of this Government to protect them in the attempt? If the principle involved in the obvious answer to these questions be abandoned, it will follow that the objects of this Government are reversed, and that it has become a part of its duty to aid in destroying the States which it was established to protect.

Duplicating any part of this book is prohibited by law.

Our conduct toward these people is deeply interesting to our national character. Their present condition, contrasted with what they once were, makes a most powerful appeal to our sympathies. Our ancestors found them the uncontrolled possessors of these vast regions. By persuasion and force they have been made to retire from river to river and from mountain to mountain, until some of the tribes have become extinct and others have left but remnants to preserve for a while their once terrible names. Surrounded by the whites with their arts of civilization, which by destroying the resources of the savage doom him to weakness and decay, the fate of the Mohegan, the Narragansett, and the Delaware is fast over-taking the Choctaw, the Cherokee, and the Creek. That this fate surely awaits them if they remain within the limits of the States does not admit of a doubt. Humanity and national honor demand that every effort should be made to avert so great a calamity. It is too late to inquire whether it was just in the United States to include them and their territory within the bounds of new States, whose limits they could control. That step cannot be retraced. A State cannot be dismembered by Congress or restricted in the exercise of her constitutional power. But the people of those States and of every State, actuated by feelings of justice and a regard for our national honor, submit to you the interesting question whether something cannot be done, consistently with the rights of the States, to preserve this much-injured race.

As a means of effecting this end I suggest for your consideration the propriety of setting apart an ample district west of the Mississippi, and without the limits of any State or Territory now formed, to be guaranteed to the Indian tribes as long as they shall occupy it, each tribe having a distinct control over the portion designated for its use. There they may be secured in the enjoyment of governments of their own choice, subject to no other control from the United States than such as may be necessary to preserve peace on the frontier and between the several tribes. There the benevolent may endeavor to teach them the arts of civilization, and, by promoting union and harmony among them, to raise up an interesting commonwealth, destined to perpetuate the race and to attest the humanity and justice of this Government.

This emigration should be voluntary, for it would be as cruel as unjust to compel the <u>aborigines</u> to abandon the graves of their fathers and seek a home in a distant land. But they should be distinctly informed that if they remain within the limits of the States they must be subject to their laws. ... Submitting to the laws of the States, and receiving, like other citizens, protection in their persons and property, they will ere long become merged in the mass of our population.

Duplicating any part of this book is prohibited by law.

19. What MOST clearly shows President Jackson's opinion about Native Americans?

   A. his references to their "tribes"

   B. his calling their ways of life "savage"

   C. his description of their claiming independence

   D. his admitting that they once freely possessed America

20. In paragraph 1 of the speech, what reason does President Jackson give for Native Americans' remaining "in a wandering state"?

   A. the interest of Americans in their fate

   B. the attempts of the U.S. government to "civilize" them

   C. the loss of much of their land

   D. their establishing independent governments within the states

21. Which BEST explains the meaning of <u>sovereigns</u> as it is used in this speech?

   A. police

   B. judges

   C. monarchs

   D. authorities

22. Read this entry from a glossary.

   aborigine   original resident of a place or region

Which word is closest in meaning to that of <u>aborigine</u>?

   A. native

   B. citizen

   C. neighbor

   D. occupant

Duplicating any part of this book is prohibited by law.

23. Which statement from this speech BEST supports the claim that President Jackson believed that the culture of Native Americans was likely to fade away?

A. "The ... destiny of the Indian tribes within the limits of some of our States have become objects of much interest and importance."

B. "Our conduct toward these people is deeply interesting to our national character."

C. "Surrounded by the whites with their arts of civilization, which by destroying the resources of the savage doom him to weakness and decay ..."

D. "There the benevolent may endeavor to teach them the arts of civilization ..."

24. How did President Jackson's vision of the Indian Removal Act, described in the last two paragraphs of this speech, compare with the actual experiences of the Cherokee when the act was put into effect?

_____

_____

_____

_____

_____

Duplicating any part of this book is prohibited by law.

Part 2: Language Arts

This passage contains mistakes. Read the passage and answer the questions that follow.

Edward Curtis and *The North American Indian*

(1) In 1900, photographer Edward Curtis began an ambitious, unprecedented project. (2) His goal was to document information about the lives and traditions of western, Native American peoples. (3) He thought that the project would take five years to complete. (4) Instead, he worked on the project for thirty years, completing the last of twenty volumes of photographs and detailed, textual commentary in 1930. (5) The entire project was called *The North American Indian*.

(6) Curtis had moved with his family to a town near Seattle, Washington, in 1887. (7) He had already learned to take photographs; and in Seattle, he quickly developed a career as a professional, studio photographer. (8) He also photographed subjects outside of the studio, including many Native Americans living in the area. (9) He won awards for some of this work.

(10) Toward the end of the century, he befriended George Bird Grinnell, who was the editor of a magazine called *Forest and Stream*. (11) Grinnell was also an expert on Native Americans and visited a tribe of Blackfoot Indians in Montana every year. (12) In 1900, Grinnell invited Curtis to come along on the trip to Montana. (13) After Curtis photographed the Blackfoot Indians, he was inspired to create a record of all the most significant Native American tribes west of the Mississippi River.

(14) Despite his interest in traditional Native American culture, Curtis shared many ideas about Native Americans that were common at the time. (15) He thought that Native American culture was very likely to disappear. (16) In fact, at first, he agreed with the policy of the U.S. government, which was trying to force Native Americans to <u>assimilate</u>, or become absorbed into mainstream society. (17) Later, however, he changed his views on assimilation.

(18) In the end, Curtis took 40,000 photographs, made 10,000 recordings, and wrote down hundreds of stories. (19) In many ways, his work is controversial. (20) For example, Curtis often did not photograph Native Americans in their <u>contemporary</u> dress or going about their normal routines. (21) He instead staged the photographs in order to portray Native Americans' older more traditional dress and customs. (22) However, the information that Curtis recorded is rich and, in some cases, is found nowhere else. (23) Scholars have used his work in their research.

Duplicating any part of this book is prohibited by law.

25. In which of the following phrases from the passage is the comma use correct?

A. an ambitious, unprecedented project

B. western, Native American peoples

C. detailed, textual commentary

D. a professional, studio photographer

26. Which of the following is a complex sentence?

A. He also photographed subjects outside of the studio, including many Native Americans living in the area.

B. Grinnell was also an expert on Native Americans and visited a tribe of Blackfoot Indians in Montana every year.

C. After Curtis photographed the Blackfoot Indians, he was inspired to create a record of all the most significant Native American tribes west of the Mississippi River.

D. He instead staged the photographs in order to portray Native Americans' older more traditional dress and customs.

27. Read sentence 16 from the passage.

> **In fact, at first, he agreed with the policy of the U.S. government, which was trying to force Native Americans to assimilate, or become absorbed into mainstream society.**

Which word or phrase from sentence 16 is analogous in meaning to <u>assimilate</u>?

A. policy

B. force

C. mainstream society

D. become absorbed

28. What does <u>contemporary</u> mean as it is used in this passage?

A. present-day

B. ordinary

C. fashionable

D. traditional

Duplicating any part of this book is prohibited by law.

29. Read sentence 21 from the passage.

He instead staged the photographs in order to portray Native Americans' older more traditional dress and customs.

What is the BEST way to punctuate sentence 21?

A. He, instead, staged the photographs in order to portray Native Americans' older more traditional dress and customs.

B. He instead staged the photographs, in order to portray Native Americans' older more traditional dress and customs.

C. He instead staged the photographs in order to portray Native Americans' older, more traditional dress and customs.

D. He instead staged the photographs in order to portray Native Americans' older more traditional dress, and customs.

30. Read sentences 22 and 23 from the passage.

However, the information that Curtis recorded is rich and, in some cases, is found nowhere else. Scholars have used his work in their research.

Rewrite these sentences, using the subordinating conjunction *because* to join them into one complex sentence.

_____

_____

_____

_____

Duplicating any part of this book is prohibited by law.

Part 3: Writing

Personal Narrative Prompt

Write a personal narrative telling about a place that you love. The place could be your room, your home, the home of a relative or friend, somewhere out-of-doors, somewhere you go often, somewhere you have been only once—or any place at all. What does this place look like to you? How do you feel and what do you do when you are there? Use details to show why you like this place so much and explain what you do there.

Use the checklist below to help you do your best writing.

Does your personal narrative

❑ have an engaging introduction?

❑ set up a clear context and have events that follow one another clearly?

❑ use transitional words and phrases to help readers follow the sequence of events?

❑ use descriptive details and/or dialogue to show setting, events, and characters?

❑ use vivid and exact words, phrases, and details?

❑ use a style and vocabulary that make sense for the audience and purpose?

❑ have a thoughtful conclusion?

❑ use correct spelling and use conventional grammar and mechanics?

Use the following pages to plan and write your response.

Duplicating any part of this book is prohibited by law.

Planning Page

Duplicating any part of this book is prohibited by law.

Duplicating any part of this book is prohibited by law.

Duplicating any part of this book is prohibited by law.

Duplicating any part of this book is prohibited by law.

Duplicating any part of this book is prohibited by law.

Benchmark Assessment 3

Duplicating any part of this book is prohibited by law.

Part 1: Reading Comprehension

Read the drama and answer the questions that follow.

The New Girl:
A Play in One Act

CAST OF CHARACTERS
Charlene
Denise
Monica
Eliza
Other middle-school students

Scene One

Groups of middle-school students are sitting, talking, and eating their lunches at three or four picnic tables on a patio outside the school cafeteria. Charlene, Denise, and Monica are sitting at a picnic table on stage left. Eliza walks out of the cafeteria, pauses, and looks around the patio, as though she is lost. She is wearing a long, tie-dyed skirt and an apparently handmade sweater. After a few moments, she walks to the very front of the stage, sits down on the patio, apart from everyone else, and begins to eat her bagged lunch.

CHARLENE: (*nudging Denise with her elbow*) Hey, look, there's that new girl.

DENISE: What on earth is she wearing?

CHARLENE: Who knows? (*shouting*) Hey, new girl! (*whispering to Denise*) She won't look over here. (*shouting more loudly*) NEW GIRL!

Eliza continues to eat her lunch, not looking toward Charlene and Denise or anyone else.

MONICA: (*quietly*) C'mon, Charlene. Leave her alone.

CHARLENE: (*ignoring Monica and shouting*) Hey, new girl! What's *up* with that outfit?

DENISE: (*shouting*) Going to visit your grandma?

Charlene, Denise, and students at another table laugh at the wisecrack.

MONICA: Going to visit your *grandma*? What is that supposed to mean?

DENISE: (*shrugging*) I don't know.

CHARLENE: You know, she dresses weird. Like it's the 1960s or something.

MONICA: So what?

Duplicating any part of this book is prohibited by law.

CHARLENE: What do you mean, so what?

MONICA: I mean so what, who cares?

DENISE: Well, for one thing, it looks dumb.

MONICA: Who cares if it looks dumb or not?

DENISE: I don't know. Maybe because we have to look at her.

MONICA: So don't look. Why are her clothes your problem? (*looking at Charlene*) Or yours?

CHARLENE: I don't have a problem. What's *your* problem? What has gotten into you?

MONICA: I don't know. It's just that … well, it's not like you're perfect, or anything. Or like any of us is perfect. Why do you need to criticize and mock people all the time? And anyway, I think … (*her voice trailing off*)

CHARLENE: (*partly scornful, partly amused*) What do you think?

MONICA: (*shrugging*) I think she looks interesting, is all.

CHARLENE and DENISE: (*together*) Interesting?

CHARLENE: Why don't you sit and talk to her then?

DENISE: Yeah, why don't you?

MONICA: Well, maybe I will!

Monica hesitates, then gets up. She walks over to where Eliza is sitting.

MONICA: Hi.

Eliza does not look up. She says nothing.

MONICA: Hi, um … can I sit here?

Eliza again does not look up. She shrugs. Monica sits down next to her.

MONICA: My name is Monica. What's yours?

ELIZA: (*ignoring the question*) Did they send you over here?

MONICA: (*looking back toward Charlene and Denise, who are whispering to each other*) Them? No, not really. I wanted to come over and say hello. I don't think … I don't think I like them very much anymore.

Duplicating any part of this book is prohibited by law.

ELIZA: You liked them before?

MONICA: They weren't always like that. They didn't used to be mean.

ELIZA: (*sighs*) Yeah, that's why I was glad to move away from my other school. So many of my friends had gotten so weird and mean. And then I come here, and it's all the same as it was there.

MONICA: Well, not everyone here is mean. Some of us are just … quieter.

ELIZA: (*smiling*) I can hear you, though, if you know what I mean. It's nice to meet you. My name is Eliza.

Bell rings.

MONICA: Hey, I have to go. My next class is all the way on the other side of the school. Meet you here for lunch tomorrow?

ELIZA: OK!

MONICA: OK, see you tomorrow!

Monica returns to the picnic table where Charlene and Denise are still sitting. She picks up her bag.

CHARLENE: So, how was the new girl?

MONICA: I like her. I like her a lot. She's a *real* friend.

Charlene and Denise look stunned as Monica walks away.

Duplicating any part of this book is prohibited by law.

1. This story is effective as a drama because its

   A. characters are middle-school students.

   B. conflict develops through dialogue.

   C. setting is a middle school.

   D. theme is about friendship.

2. Monica could BEST be described as

   A. guilty.

   B. sad.

   C. confused.

   D. sympathetic.

3. What does Monica mean when she says, "Going to visit your *grandma*?" What does her tone reveal?

   A. She thinks that Denise's question is silly.

   B. She is really confused by Denise's question.

   C. She would like to visit her own grandma.

   D. She is amused by Denise's question.

4. Why is Eliza unfriendly to Monica at first?

   A. She is not a friendly person.

   B. She prefers to be alone.

   C. She thinks that Monica intends to be mean.

   D. She misses her old school.

Duplicating any part of this book is prohibited by law.

5. When Eliza says that her friends at her other school became "weird," she MOST LIKELY means that

    A. they became scary.

    B. their behavior changed.

    C. they became much less popular.

    D. they were influenced by the supernatural.

6. When Monica tells Eliza that the students at their school who are not mean are also quieter than those who are mean, Eliza says, "I can hear you, though …" What are the literal and figurative meanings of Eliza's statement?

_____

_____

_____

_____

Duplicating any part of this book is prohibited by law.

Read the passage and answer the questions that follow.

Gifts from China

Guided by compasses, sailors set out to explore the mysteries of unknown shores. With guns and cannons blazing, ordinary farmers faced British troops in the American Revolution. People around the world drink tea, read books, and fly kites. What do compasses, gunpowder, cannons, tea, printing presses, and kites all have in common? They had their origins in China.

Tea

The Chinese began to use tea leaves as long ago as 2700 BCE. At first, they used tea as a medicine and to help digestion. Over time, it became a popular drink. By 300 CE, it had become a daily drink; and by 700 CE, China had numerous teashops and many books about tea.

Over the centuries, tea spread from China to the rest of the world. Around 800 CE, tea seeds were brought to Japan. Then, in the 1600s, the Dutch East India Company brought tea to Europe for the first time. As was already true for spices and silk, tea became an important trade item. By 1830, the British were importing 300 million pounds of tea from China each year. They even built swift ships called *clippers* for this tea trade. In the 1800s and 1900s, tea also began to be grown throughout the world—not only in Asian countries but also in Africa, North and South America, and Australia.

Compasses

The Chinese contributed to trade in another important way. Long sea voyages would not have been possible without the compass, another Chinese invention.

For the Chinese, certain directions were luckier than others. They invented a special instrument, the compass, to help them locate the most favorable spot to build a house or to place a grave. Chinese compasses were used to indicate south, the most important direction to the Chinese people.

The first compasses appeared around 100 CE. They used magnetic stones shaped like a fish or a spoon to show directions. The first compasses with needles were made around 570 CE. Compasses were not used for sailing until about 1100.

Compasses reached Europe about two hundred years later, in 1300. Columbus set sail for India with thirty or forty compass needles. There had to be plenty in case some were lost or broken. Without compasses, there would have been far fewer long voyages of discovery. History would have been very different, indeed.

Gunpowder

Many historians state that the Chinese invented gunpowder around 600 CE. Of course, nobody called it gunpowder then because the first guns weren't even made until the 1300s. The first gunpowder is sometimes called black powder because of its color. It is a mixture of sulfur, charcoal, and a substance called *saltpeter*. When mixed properly, black powder burns quickly, producing gas. If the gas is kept in a small space, its pressure builds up and can be used to propel an object such as a bullet.

Duplicating any part of this book is prohibited by law.

The Chinese used gunpowder for their most fantastic invention: fireworks. By the 1200s, fireworks had spread to other parts of the world, and they were even being made in Europe.

Paper and Printing

China was also the birthplace of paper, but the paper that the Chinese started using around two thousand years ago was different from the paper we use today. It was a thick, spongy material made from many kinds of plants and plant components, including tree bark, straw, and seaweed. It was good for making clothing, shoes, blankets, and even armor.

The invention of paper also helped the Chinese government organize its official documents. Before paper, documents had to be written on silk or on bulky pieces of wood. This new material was easier to use and to store.

However, copying books by hand was slow and expensive. Chinese inventors looked for a better, more efficient way to make lots of copies of books. By 710 CE, the Chinese had produced the first block prints. A block print is like a giant stamp—with words carved into wood. Printers could make hundreds of copies of a page from one block.

The Chinese also experimented with moveable type, sticking tiny blocks together on a plate coated with a mixture of resin, wax, and paper ash to produce a type of page. Around 1450 in Germany, Johannes Gutenberg "borrowed" this idea to create Europe's first printing press. By 1500, an estimated 20 million books were in print. With all these books, people were able to spread information and ideas faster than ever before.

The inventions of paper and printing have had an enormous influence on people around the world. People can get newspapers delivered to their door or curl up with a good mystery novel. And just think … if traders had not carried those inventions around the world, you might not be reading these words!

Inventing Moveable Type: A Comparison

	In China	In Europe
When Was It Invented?	about 1041–1048	about 1450
Who Invented It?	Pi Sheng, a chemist	Johannes Gutenberg, a goldsmith
What Was the Type Made Of?	a mixture of clay and glue	a mixture of lead, tin, and antimony
What Was the Type Set In?	a plate coated with a mixture of resin, wax, and paper ash	galley trays

Duplicating any part of this book is prohibited by law.

7. According to the passage, for what purpose did the Chinese invent the compass?

    A. to navigate at sea

    B. to locate fortunate sites

    C. to find a route to Europe

    D. to help them expand trade

8. Which sentence from the passage includes an opinion?

    A. "Many historians state that the Chinese invented gunpowder around 600 CE."

    B. "The first gunpowder is sometimes called black powder because of its color."

    C. "When mixed properly, black powder burns quickly, producing gas."

    D. "The Chinese used gunpowder for their most fantastic invention: fireworks."

9. Read this sentence from the passage.

    By 1500, an estimated 20 million books were in print.

    Which is the BEST inference that can be made from this sentence?

    A. Before moveable type, people did not read.

    B. Before moveable type, books were much more rare.

    C. Before moveable type, many books were banned.

    D. Before moveable type, people were uninterested in books.

10. Why is the claim that Johannes Gutenberg "borrowed" the idea of moveable type from the Chinese believable?

    A. It was invented in China much earlier than in Europe.

    B. He and Pi Sheng had similar professions.

    C. His type was made of materials similar to those used by the Chinese.

    D. The typesetting process in Europe was identical to that used in China.

Duplicating any part of this book is prohibited by law.

11. Which text structure is used in the section titled "Paper and Printing"?

    A. cause and effect

    B. problem and solution

    C. compare and contrast

    D. chronological order

12. Write a 2–3 sentence summary of the section titled "Tea."

    _____

    _____

    _____

    _____

    _____

Duplicating any part of this book is prohibited by law.

Read the poem and answer the questions that follow.

A Conservative
by Charlotte Perkins Gilman

The garden beds I wandered by
   One bright and cheerful morn,
When I found a new-fledged[1] butterfly,
   A-sitting on a thorn,
5 A black and crimson butterfly
   All doleful and forlorn.

I thought that life could have no <u>sting</u>
   To infant butterflies,
So I gazed on this unhappy thing
10   With wonder and surprise.
While sadly with his waving wing
   He wiped his weeping eyes.

Said I, "What can the matter be?
   Why weepest thou so sore?
15 With garden fair and sunlight free
   And flowers in goodly store,"[2]—
But he only turned away from me
   And burst into a roar.

[1] **new-fledged** having new wings
[2] **goodly store** in abundance

Duplicating any part of this book is prohibited by law.

Cried he, "My legs are thin and few
20   Where once I had a swarm!
Soft fuzzy fur—a joy to view—
        Once kept my body warm,
Before these flapping wing-things grew,
        To hamper and deform!"

25   At that outrageous bug I shot
        The fury of mine eye;
Said I, in scorn all burning hot,
        In rage and anger high,
"You ignominious[3] idiot!
30   Those wings are made to fly!"

"I do not want to fly," said he,
        "I only want to squirm!"
And he drooped his wings dejectedly,
        But still his voice was firm:
35   "I do not want to be a fly!
        I want to be a worm!"

O yesterday of unknown lack
        To-day of unknown bliss!
I left my fool in red and black;
40   The last I saw was this,—
The creature madly climbing back
        Into his chrysalis.

<hr>

[3] **ignominious** shameful

Duplicating any part of this book is prohibited by law.

13. The form of this poem could BEST be described as

    A. narrative, or telling a story.

    B. lyric, or creating a mood.

    C. epic, or retelling heroic deeds.

    D. elegiac, or expressing grief.

14. What characteristic of the poem does its singsong, or bouncing, meter emphasize?

    A. the speaker's delight

    B. the speaker's longing

    C. the speaker's confusion

    D. the speaker's ironic humor

15. Which BEST explains the meaning of <u>sting</u> as it is used in stanza 2?

    A. a wound from an insect

    B. a sharp body part

    C. a mental pain or difficulty

    D. a criminal operation

16. By saying that he wants to be a worm, the butterfly means that he prefers

    A. to crawl

    B. to eat dirt

    C. to be blind

    D. to hide

Duplicating any part of this book is prohibited by law.

17. To the speaker of the poem, what does the butterfly's ability to fly symbolize?

    A. beauty

    B. joy

    C. old age

    D. sadness

18. In stanza 5 of the poem, the speaker expresses anger toward the butterfly. Using details from the poem, explain why the speaker is angry.

    _____

    _____

    _____

    _____

    _____

Duplicating any part of this book is prohibited by law.

Read the poem and answer the questions that follow.

A Summer Afternoon
by James Whitcomb Riley

A languid atmosphere, a lazy breeze,
    With labored respiration[1], moves the wheat
From distant reaches, till the golden seas
    Break in crisp whispers at my feet.

5   My book, neglected of an idle mind,
    Hides for a moment from the eyes of men;
Or lightly opened by a critic wind,
    Affrightedly reviews itself again.

Off through the haze that dances in the shine
10   The warm sun showers in the open glade,
The forest lies, a silhouette design
    Dimmed through and through with shade.

A dreamy day; and tranquilly I lie
    At anchor from all storms of mental strain;
15 With absent vision, gazing at the sky,
    "Like one that hears it rain."

The Katydid, so boisterous last night,
    Clinging, inverted, in uneasy poise,
Beneath a wheat-blade, has forgotten quite
20   If "Katy DID or DIDN'T" make a noise.

The twitter, sometimes, of a wayward bird
    That checks the song abruptly at the sound,
And mildly, chiding echoes that have stirred,
    Sink into silence, all the more profound.

25 And drowsily I hear the plaintive strain[2]
    Of some poor dove ... Why, I can scarcely keep
My heavy eyelids—there it is again—
    "Coo-coo!"—I mustn't—"Coo-coo!"—fall asleep!

---

[1] **respiration** breathing
[2] **plaintive strain** sorrowful melody

Duplicating any part of this book is prohibited by law.

19. Which word from stanza 1 often has a negative connotation?

   A. distant

   B. lazy

   C. golden

   D. crisp

20. Read lines 13–14 from the poem.

   **A dreamy day; and tranquilly I lie
   At anchor from all storms of
   mental strain;**

   In these lines, the speaker compares himself to

   A. a dream.

   B. bad weather.

   C. a headache.

   D. a boat or ship.

21. The imagery in stanzas 5–7 emphasizes the

   A. sights that the speaker sees.

   B. sounds that the speaker hears.

   C. scents that the speaker smells.

   D. sensations that the speaker feels.

22. The dashes in stanza 7 show what characteristic of the speaker?

   A. excitement

   B. happiness

   C. sleepiness

   D. irritation

Duplicating any part of this book is prohibited by law.

23. How does the feeling expressed by the speaker in "A Summer Afternoon" compare with that expressed by the speaker in "A Conservative"?

A. The speaker in "A Summer Afternoon" is more relaxed.

B. The speaker in "A Summer Afternoon" is sad rather than angry.

C. The speaker in "A Summer Afternoon" is studious rather than confused.

D. The speaker in "A Summer Afternoon" is more critical.

24. What are the similarities in the meter and rhyme patterns of "A Summer Afternoon" and "A Conservative"?

_____

_____

_____

_____

_____

Duplicating any part of this book is prohibited by law.

Part 2: Language Arts

This passage contains mistakes. Read the passage and answer the questions that follow.

The Night of the Eclipse

(1) That was the summer we saw a lunar eclipse. (2) My mother, my sister, and I decided to go to the beach that night. (3) What better place is there to see the moon disappear than over the ocean, where the sky and the stars are both as big as can be?

(4) "Looks like we aren't the only ones who had this idea," said Katie, my sister, after we made our way down the boardwalk through the dunes and onto the beach. (5) Sitting on blankets and chairs and looking up at the sky, we saw dozens of people already there. (6) One group of people had even built a bonfire.

(7) "I guess if it's a good idea, others are bound to have it, too," said Mom. (8) "Let's find a spot to sit."

(9) We spread our blanket on a spot to the side of the crowd. (10) I kicked off my sandals and sat down on the edge of the blanket so that I could bury my feet in the soft sand. (11) It was still warm from the day's heat.

(12) "Just look at the moon," I said. (13) "It doesn't look anything like I thought it would." (14) Instead of glowing its usual pale yellow, it seemed to be on fire, burning an eerie orange-red. (15) Its left edge had already begun to disappear, as though it were fading into the dark night sky.

(16) "I don't know what I expected," said Katie, "but it's as though it's being erased. (17) It's a little spooky."

(18) "Just imagine," said Mom. (19) "That's Earth's shadow out there—*our* shadow."

(20) We ate brownies that Mom had made. (21) Katie got drowsy, and I had to keep poking her awake. (22) I was wide awake and enjoying this strange fascinating evening. (23) We sat and listened to the rhythmic roar of the ocean and watched the moon disappear. (24) It vanished right before our eyes, but so slowly—much more slowly than I had imagined it would—until just the smallest sliver was left. (25) I breathed in and breathed out, and in a moment it was gone.

(26) There was a patch of star-less night where the moon had been. (27) But that blank spot wasn't really part of the night sky. (28) Just as Mom said, it was us—*our* shadow.

Duplicating any part of this book is prohibited by law.

25. Read sentence 3 from the passage.

What better place is there to see the moon disappear than over the ocean, where the sky and the stars are both as big as can be?

In sentence 3, the relative clause <u>where the sky and the stars are both as big as can be</u> modifies which word?

A. better

B. see

C. moon

D. ocean

26. Read sentence 5 from the passage.

Sitting on blankets and chairs and looking up at the sky, we saw dozens of people already there.

What is the BEST way to rewrite sentence 5?

A. We saw dozens of people already there, sitting on blankets and chairs and looking up at the sky.

B. We saw dozens sitting on blankets and chairs and looking up at the sky, people already there.

C. We saw dozens of people sitting on blankets and chairs and looking up at the sky, already there.

D. We saw, sitting on blankets and chairs and looking up at the sky, dozens of people already there.

27. Read sentence 9 from the passage.

We spread our blanket on a spot to the side of the crowd.

In sentence 9, the prepositional phrase <u>on a spot</u> modifies which word?

A. We

B. spread

C. blanket

D. side

28. Read sentence 15 from the passage.

Its left edge had already begun to disappear, as though it were fading into the dark night sky.

Which word in sentence 15 is LEAST necessary and should be deleted?

A. left

B. already

C. as

D. dark

Duplicating any part of this book is prohibited by law.

29. Read sentence 22 from the passage.

   I was wide awake and enjoying this strange fascinating evening.

   What is the BEST way to punctuate sentence 22?

   A. I was wide awake, and enjoying this strange fascinating evening.

   B. I was wide awake and enjoying, this strange fascinating evening.

   C. I was wide awake and enjoying this strange, fascinating evening.

   D. I was wide awake and enjoying this strange, fascinating, evening.

30. Read sentences 10 and 11 from the passage.

   I kicked off my sandals and sat down on the edge of the blanket so that I could bury my feet in the soft sand. It was still warm from the day's heat.

   Combine these sentences into one, using the relative pronoun *which* to create a subordinate clause.

   _____

   _____

   _____

   _____

   _____

Duplicating any part of this book is prohibited by law.

Part 3: Writing

Fictional Narrative Prompt

Even the best of friends can find themselves competing with each other. Write a fictional narrative telling about two friends who are in competition with each other. They could both be trying out for the same part in a play, they could be competing to become captain of their soccer team, or they could simply be playing against each other in a pick-up game of basketball. What aspects of their characters become most obvious in the conflict? What do they learn about each other, themselves, and their friendship?

Use the checklist below to help you do your best writing.

Does your fictional narrative

❏ introduce a narrator and/or characters?

❏ set up a situation clearly and have events that follow one another clearly?

❏ use transitional words and phrases to help readers follow the sequence of events?

❏ use descriptive details and/or dialogue to show events and characters?

❏ use vivid and exact words, phrases, and details?

❏ use a style and vocabulary that make sense for the audience and purpose?

❏ have an interesting conclusion?

❏ use correct spelling and use conventional grammar and mechanics?

Use the following pages to plan and write your response.

Duplicating any part of this book is prohibited by law.

Planning Page

Duplicating any part of this book is prohibited by law.

Duplicating any part of this book is prohibited by law.

Duplicating any part of this book is prohibited by law.

Duplicating any part of this book is prohibited by law.

Duplicating any part of this book is prohibited by law.

Benchmark Assessment 4

Duplicating any part of this book is prohibited by law.

Part 1: Reading Comprehension

Read the passage and answer the questions that follow.

South for the Winter and Back Again

About two-thirds of the species of birds found in the United States migrate south for the winter. Some birds head to the Gulf States, and others go as far as South America. Most, however, spend their winters throughout Mexico and Central America, which has the greatest density of wintering birds in the world.

Why Do Birds Migrate?

Most species of birds have a high metabolic rate. In other words, their bodies rapidly turn their food into energy. For this reason, birds need to eat frequently. During the winter, the food supply for certain birds becomes inadequate for their needs. Therefore, they travel from their northern breeding grounds to where they can get food for the winter.

Not all migrating birds are originally from the north, however. Some birds, such as hummingbirds, orioles, and swifts, are originally from the southern tropics. As weather conditions changed in the distant past, these birds started flying north in the spring so that they could breed where there was less competition for nesting grounds and food. They would return to their original habitat in the winter.

Whether their ancestors are originally from the south or from the north, birds do not choose to migrate. Instead, they are programmed to do so. As the length of the day changes, migrating birds' brains change. Their bodies begin to store fat. They join flocks of others of their species. They even become more restless. Other environmental factors, such as temperature, also influence the timing of migrating birds' departure. Good timing is essential. For example, they do not want to return to their breeding grounds in the north too early, before food is available. Nor do they want to return too late. They need to mate and bear their young early in the year so that the next generation is mature enough in the fall for the flight back to the wintering grounds.

How Do Birds Get Where They Are Going?

Migratory birds use a variety of navigation techniques. They follow mountain ranges or waterways, such as rivers or coastlines. They use other visual landmarks, as well as the sun (if they fly by day) and constellations (if they fly by night). Most remarkable, however, is that their brains contain a mineral called *magnetite*. It is believed that this mineral helps them use the magnetic fields of the earth to find their way. Apparently, migratory birds truly have an internal compass!

Duplicating any part of this book is prohibited by law.

The migration routes of each individual species are unique to that species. However, through studies of migratory routes in the mid-twentieth century, researchers discovered general patterns in the migration of bird populations. In North America, migratory routes tend to follow one of four broad north-south bands called *flyways*. The Atlantic flyway generally follows the Atlantic Coast, the Mississippi flyway generally follows the Mississippi River, the Central flyway generally follows the Central Plains and Rocky Mountains, and the Pacific flyway generally follows the Pacific Coast. As the flyways continue south, they gradually blend until they join in Panama and then spread out again along separate routes through South America. Of course, this description is of a general pattern in these migratory routes. For example, the migratory routes of many birds do not reach South America.

North American Flyways

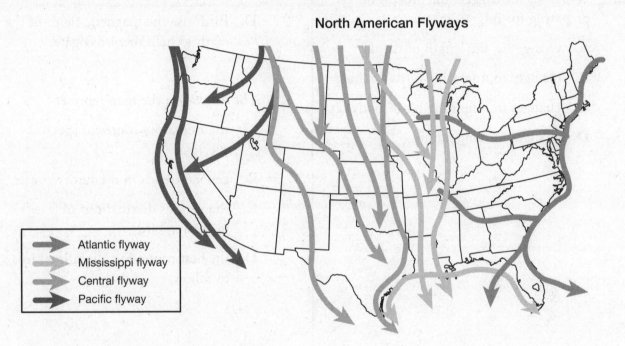

Atlantic flyway
Mississippi flyway
Central flyway
Pacific flyway

How Fast Do Migrating Birds Fly?

Most migrating birds fly at speeds from fifteen to forty-five miles per hour, and larger birds tend to be faster than smaller birds. At these speeds, a one-way trip can take a few weeks or as long as four months, and the journey is usually made in a series of several flights, with rest stops along the way. Each individual flight can last several hours—or even several days. Many species cover hundreds of miles per day until they arrive at their destination.

Some migrating birds are astonishing endurance athletes. The blackpoll warbler, for example, travels two thousand miles to South America from Canada and New England in one nonstop flight that takes seventy two hours or more. The most remarkable migrating bird, however, is the arctic tern. Traveling a total of 22,000 miles every year, the arctic tern makes its breeding grounds in the Arctic and its wintering grounds on the other side of the globe, in the Antarctic.

Duplicating any part of this book is prohibited by law.

1. Which text structure is used in paragraph 2?

   A. cause and effect

   B. compare and contrast

   C. chronological order

   D. order of importance

2. Which factor triggers the process of preparing for migration?

   A. changes in the length of the day

   B. changes in migrating birds' brains

   C. changes in migrating birds' body fat

   D. changes in temperature

3. Which idea about the navigation techniques of migrating birds seems to be based on speculation rather than fact?

   A. Birds use mountain ranges or waterways to help them navigate.

   B. Birds use visual landmarks to help them navigate.

   C. Birds use the sun and constellations to help them navigate.

   D. Birds use the magnetic fields of the earth to help them navigate.

4. The arrows on the map represent

   A. the migratory routes of specific species.

   B. general trends in migratory routes.

   C. the various destinations of migrating birds.

   D. the best routes for migrating birds to follow.

Duplicating any part of this book is prohibited by law.

5. What can be concluded about the major North American flyways from the text and the map?

    A. Each flyway is distinct from the others.

    B. Many more birds migrate south than return north.

    C. The flyways are broadly defined and even overlap.

    D. The Atlantic flyway is the most popular route.

6. Why does the author characterize certain migrating birds as "astonishing endurance athletes"? Give evidence from the passage to support this claim.

_____

_____

_____

_____

_____

Duplicating any part of this book is prohibited by law.

Read the passage and answer the questions that follow.

Bird Blind Basics

So you want to take up bird watching? Of course, one good option is to go where the birds are. But why not let the birds come to you? With a bird blind and a lot of patience, you just might be able to get close to birds that have no idea that you're even there.

A **bird blind** is any structure that is designed to shield you from the view of birds. It could be made from a box, or it could be constructed like a tent. You can even use a car as a bird blind! Obviously, your blind must do more than just hide you from the birds. It needs to include a way for you to look out and see them—or even photograph them.

The following are the key characteristics of a good bird blind:

- **It should be sturdy.** You don't want your bird blind to fall down or blow away!
- **It should be comfortable.** Even with a bird blind, it might take a while for interesting birds to come within your sight. Give yourself lots of space in the blind, and consider placing a pillow, stool, or chair inside to sit on.
- **It should be made of a material that light cannot penetrate.** Even just casting a shadow can keep wildlife away. Therefore, if you are making a tent-like structure for your bird blind, use heavy canvas.
- **It should be hidden or disguised.** The less obvious both you and the bird blind itself are, the more birds you are likely to see.

Another important consideration in using a bird blind is deciding where to place it. You want to place your bird blind in a location where birds tend to gather. For example, if you're going to put the blind in your own yard, the best location to place it might be within view of a bird feeder, if you have one.

Once you have found a good location, follow these steps to make a basic bird blind:

1. **Gather the necessary materials.** These might include a cardboard box large enough for you to sit inside, such as a box that contained a refrigerator; a marker; a pair of sturdy scissors or a utility knife; and green and brown paints or markers.
2. **Decide where to cut a window in the box.** Get inside the box, and get comfortable. If you plan to use a pillow, stool, or chair when you use your bird blind, bring it into the box and sit on it. Draw a rectangle at eye level on the side of the box where you want the window. (See diagram.)
3. **Cut the window out of the box.** Use a pair of sturdy scissors or utility knife to cut out the rectangle that you outlined.
4. **Camouflage the box.** Use green and brown paints or markers to draw grass, bushes, or trees on all sides of the box—whatever will help it blend into the location where you plan to place your bird blind. You can even attach actual branches and leaves to its sides!

Duplicating any part of this book is prohibited by law.

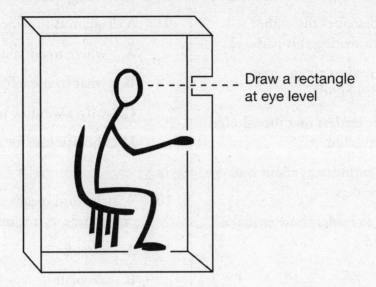

Draw a rectangle at eye level

In these four simple steps, you've transformed a simple cardboard box into a bird blind! Now place it in the location you have chosen for it and get your pillow, stool, or chair, along with your field guide, binoculars, and camera. Wait quietly and patiently—and soon enough, the birds will be coming into view. Over time, you will learn to identify birds not only by their markings but also by their behavior: how they move, what they eat, and how they interact with other birds of their own species and other species. Just imagine learning all that from a seat in your own backyard!

Duplicating any part of this book is prohibited by law.

7. Which BEST describes the author's main purpose in writing this passage?

A. to inform readers about various kinds of bird blinds

B. to persuade readers that they should build a bird blind

C. to express enthusiasm about bird blinds to readers

D. to explain to readers how to make a bird blind

8. When making a bird blind, for what reason should you get inside the box before you cut a window into it?

A. to make sure that the box is comfortable

B. to make sure that you have chosen a large enough box

C. to make sure that light does not penetrate the box

D. to make sure that you cut the window in the best place

9. A diagram is provided in order to clarify

A. where to cut a window.

B. what to use in cutting a window.

C. why a window is needed.

D. the best size for a window.

10. Which word means the same as camouflage as it is used in this passage?

A. disguise

B. decorate

C. color

D. complete

Duplicating any part of this book is prohibited by law.

11. What can be learned from using a bird blind that CANNOT be learned from reading an article such as "South for the Winter and Back Again"?

A. the migratory patterns of North American birds

B. the day-to-day behavior of specific birds

C. the environmental factors that influence bird migration

D. the distances traveled by birds that breed or stop in your area

12. How are the characteristics of birds that interest the authors of "South for the Winter and Back Again" and "Bird Blind Basics" similar or different?

_____

_____

_____

_____

_____

Duplicating any part of this book is prohibited by law.

The Worst Week

Jonah was having the worst week of his life so far.

As most bad weeks do, this one started on a Monday. Over the weekend, Jonah had completely forgotten about the test that Mr. Wilson, his math teacher, would be giving on Monday. Jonah hadn't studied a bit. After all, who gives tests on Mondays? Apparently, Mr. Wilson did. Jonah left class feeling a bit sick to his stomach and was unable to finish his lunch. He hadn't been able to finish the test, either.

On Tuesday, as he left his second-period English class and sped down the hallway toward his third-period Spanish class, Jonah tripped. No, he didn't just trip—he *fell*. In fact, he didn't just fall—he landed sprawling on the floor, his books and notebooks flying in all directions. Not only did everyone in sight burst out laughing, but whispers and giggles followed him all throughout the rest of the day.

On Wednesday, Jonah got back the math test from Monday. His grade was as low as he had dreaded. Mr. Wilson seemed positively gleeful as he handed the paper with its big red "D+" back to Jonah. "Next time, young son"—for some reason, Mr. Wilson called all the boys *young son*—"it might be a good idea to study." *No kidding,* thought Jonah.

Thursday, however, was the worst day of all. Late that afternoon at baseball practice, while dashing to catch a routine fly ball, Jonah landed oddly—and hard, and painfully—on the side of his foot, which soon began to swell and bruise.

"Probably a sprain," said his coach, "but there might be a fracture." And so Jonah and his dad ended up spending much of the evening waiting in the emergency room for an X-ray. There was no break, just a sprain—*plus*, thought Jonah, *a wasted evening and a week or two with no baseball.*

That's it, he said to himself. *No way am I going to school tomorrow. I don't even want to know what could happen if I dare to get out of bed.*

As it turned out, his parents agreed. "The doctor said to stay off the foot for a while," said his mom. "Anyway, I don't like the idea of you going to school after such a late, stressful night."

Friday started off wonderfully. Jonah slept in, with the cat purring at his feet. At ten o'clock, when he would usually be in Spanish class, he woke to bright mid-morning sunshine. His parents had left a bagel and a pile of his favorite comic books next to his bed. Jonah propped himself up, ate the bagel, and read his comic books through the rest of the morning and into the afternoon.

Duplicating any part of this book is prohibited by law.

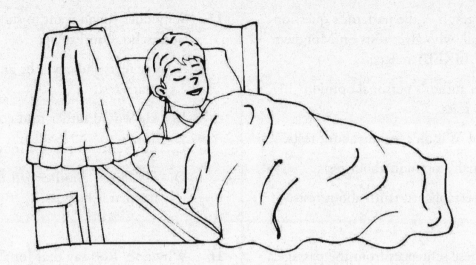

At about three o'clock, his mom returned home. "How's the foot?" she asked.

"Much better," said Jonah. In fact, the pain had gone away so completely that he had more or less forgotten about the sprain.

As his mother was helping Jonah get downstairs to the living room couch, his friend Rob came over. "Feeling better?" he asked.

"Yeah," said Jonah. "Did I miss anything at school?"

"Don't you remember?" asked Rob.

"Remember what?"

"Today was the annual spring picnic! It was great! No classes after fourth period. There was a make-your-own-sundae bar this year. And a bunch of silly games—kids' games, like three-legged races. But still, it was fun. I came in third in the sack race."

"Sack race?" said Jonah, stunned.

"Yeah, you know, where you jump around in a bag …"

"I know what a sack race is," said Jonah. "It's just that I can't believe it. If I go to school, something bad happens. But then if I don't go to school, I miss out on something good."

"Just your luck this week, I guess," said Rob.

"Maybe so. Or maybe I should start doing a better job of remembering things. You know, like math tests and spring picnics."

"And maybe you should get a little less clumsy?"

Jonah laughed. "Yes, that, too!"

Duplicating any part of this book is prohibited by law.

13. In paragraph 2, the narrator's question "After all, who gives tests on Mondays?" MOST LIKELY reflects

    A. the author's personal opinion on tests.

    B. Mr. Wilson's feeling about tests.

    C. Jonah's opinion about tests.

    D. an established truth about tests.

14. Read these sentences from the passage.

> **No, he didn't just trip—he *fell*. In fact, he didn't just fall—he landed sprawling on the floor, his books and notebooks flying in all directions.**

In these sentences, why does the narrator emphasize the difference between tripping, falling, and sprawling?

    A. to emphasize Jonah's injury

    B. to emphasize Jonah's embarrassment

    C. to emphasize Jonah's speed

    D. to emphasize Jonah's amusement

15. Why does Jonah want to stay home from school on Friday?

    A. He fears there will be another math test.

    B. He would rather read comic books.

    C. He wants to rest his foot.

    D. He thinks another bad thing will happen if he goes.

16. Why does Rob say that Jonah is clumsy?

    A. In one week, Jonah trips and falls and also injures his foot.

    B. Rob thinks that Jonah would be unlikely to do well in a sack race.

    C. Jonah forgot both his test and the annual spring picnic.

    D. Rob sees that Jonah needs help getting to the couch.

Duplicating any part of this book is prohibited by law.

17. Which BEST describes Jonah's attitude about his bad week at the end of the passage?

    A. sad

    B. proud

    C. amused

    D. confused

18. At the end of the passage, Jonah expresses an idea about luck. What is the theme of this passage in regard to luck? Explain.

    _____

    _____

    _____

    _____

    _____

Duplicating any part of this book is prohibited by law.

The Ocean: A Better Frontier
by Oscar Newman

In early 2010, President Obama announced plans for a new direction for NASA. These plans included the cancellation of the Constellation program, which was an effort to design and build new spacecraft to replace the space shuttles, which were retired in 2011. With the cancellation of this program, the United States effectively abandoned its plans to return to the moon by 2020, a goal set by President George W. Bush in 2003. This change in plans has dismayed many, including former astronauts Neil Armstrong, Eugene Cernan, and James Lovell. Noting that Obama's vision for NASA includes plans for longer journeys to Mars and to asteroids, as well as an increase of $6 billion to NASA's budget, I must admit that I am dismayed as well, though not for the same reasons as our esteemed former astronauts. I believe that we should be investing our efforts—and funds—in the exploration not of deep space, but of a place much closer to home: the deep ocean.

Perhaps space seems more alluring, more exotic. After all, the moon and stars have long been seen as the stuff of dreams. However, the creatures of the deep sea are more exotic than anything that could be found on the moon or Mars. Just think: At depths of four thousand meters, the water pressure is crushing, temperatures are near freezing, and there is no sunlight. And yet, even at these depths, there is life: blind lobsters, transparent squid, and gorgeous jellies. We need not go so far as space to find alien life!

Indeed, I would argue that it is the very fact that the ocean surrounds us that makes it a compelling subject for our research. Did life not begin in the ocean, in conditions much like those found near hydrothermal vents in the ocean floor? Do we not depend on the ocean, not only for the food it provides, but also for the crucial role it plays in our atmosphere, climate, and weather? Most oxygen in the atmosphere, in fact, originates in the ocean. Also, the ocean is the world's largest carbon sink, absorbing most of its organic carbon. Unfortunately, in recent years, the ocean has been suffering. For example, parts of the Pacific have been found to be depleted of oxygen. Furthermore, as more carbon dioxide is released into the atmosphere, the ocean is becoming more acidic, threatening the home of 97 percent of all life forms in the world, including plankton.

You may wonder, why should we care about plankton? We should care because plankton releases much of the oxygen we breathe into the atmosphere. As oceanographer and deep-sea explorer Sylvia Earle puts it, the ocean is "our life support system," driving the water cycle, carbon cycle, oxygen cycle, and nitrogen cycle—all the cycles on which life on Earth depends. As the human population of Earth grows beyond seven billion, we have a responsibility to understand this essential feature of the planet that sustains us. Let's look to the frontier beyond our shores. It just might be our salvation.

Duplicating any part of this book is prohibited by law.

The Deep Sea: An Undiscovered Treasure Trove

by Silvia Fox

The exploration of the ocean floor just might lead to more than an understanding of such natural disasters as earthquakes, volcanoes, and tsunamis. It could also add to the store of medicines that humans use to treat a variety of ailments.

Many of Earth's tectonic plates meet at ocean ridges far below the surface. Cracks form in Earth's crust near these ridges. A *hydrothermal vent* develops when cold ocean water seeps into the crust through one of these cracks. The water gets hot and dissolves minerals from the molten rock under the surface. Eventually, the heated fluid erupts, releasing the minerals into the surrounding water.

These conditions would be deadly to most known creatures. However, there are organisms that have adapted to life near a hydrothermal vent. Many of the adaptations that enable these creatures to survive involve chemicals that can be used to treat bone injuries and cardiovascular diseases, among other ailments. Through deep-sea exploration, we might just find cures for other problems.

Duplicating any part of this book is prohibited by law.

19. Which is the main reason why the author of "The Ocean: A Better Frontier" thinks that the ocean is a more important place to explore than outer space?

A. The ocean is more exotic than the moon or Mars.

B. The ocean is closer and cheaper to explore.

C. The ocean is necessary to life on Earth.

D. The ocean is where life began.

20. Why does the author of "The Ocean: A Better Frontier" MOST LIKELY describe the former astronauts Neil Armstrong, Eugene Cernan, and James Lovell as "esteemed"?

A. to show agreement with them

B. to show respect for them

C. to show contempt for their opinion

D. to show awe at their achievements

21. In arguing in favor of exploring the ocean, the author of "The Ocean: A Better Frontier" assumes that

A. ways to keep the ocean healthy will be discovered.

B. alien life will never be found anywhere but Earth.

C. ocean exploration is less expensive than space exploration.

D. the space program is doomed to fail.

22. Why does the author of "The Ocean: A Better Frontier" quote Sylvia Earle?

A. to show why plankton are necessary

B. to help describe the various cycles on Earth

C. to provide expert testimony as support

D. to explain why life depends on the ocean

Duplicating any part of this book is prohibited by law.

23. Answering which question would provide the BEST additional support for the argument in "The Deep Sea: An Undiscovered Treasure Trove"?

    A. What kinds of medicines are made from plants found on land?

    B. Why are the chemicals found in deep-sea creatures special?

    C. What types of bone injuries can be treated with medicines?

    D. Why are the conditions near hydrothermal vents typically deadly?

24. The authors of "The Ocean: A Better Frontier" and "The Deep Sea: An Undiscovered Treasure Trove" present different reasons for exploring the ocean. In what ways are the values represented in their arguments similar and different?

    _____

    _____

    _____

    _____

Duplicating any part of this book is prohibited by law.

This passage contains mistakes. Read the passage and answer the questions that follow.

All the Birds of Shakespeare

(1) The following lines from the play *Henry IV* by William Shakespeare are the oregin of a widespred biological threat to bird species and crops in North America: "The king forbade my tonge to speak of Mortimer. (2) But I will find him when he is asleep, and in his ear I'll holler 'Mortimer!' (3) Nay I'll have a starling shall be taught to speak nothing but 'Mortimer,' and give it to him to keep his anger still in motion."

(4) The culprit in these lines is the reference to the starling, a bird that in Shakespeare's time lived only in Europe and Asia. (5) Of course, about three centuries after he wrote this play, Shakespeare could not have predicted what would be done because of these lines.

(6) In the late nineteenth century, a New Yorker named Eugene Schiffelin decided that all the birds mentioned in Shakespeare's plays should be brought to the United States. (7) Therefore, in 1890, he released dozens of starlings (some accounts say sixty birds, and others say one hundred) into Central Park.

(8) The practice of bringing species from the Old World to the New World was <u>commen</u> at the time. (9) Many of these species could not adapt to the environment, so they died out. (10) Other species adapted very well, and some of these species, such as the starling, became a problem.

(11) The starling adapted to life in North America so well, in fact, that within sixty years the birds had spread throughout the continent as far as the Pacific Ocean. (12) It is estimated that by the start of the twenty-first century, the descendants of the original population of a few dozen numbered some 200 million birds. (13) The starling has been so successful here for a number of reasons. (14) First, starlings do not require a specific type of habitat. (15) They can <u>live</u> in a variety of kinds of places. (16) Similarly, including seeds, fruits, and invertebrates, starlings can eat just about anything. (17) Finally, they are suited for life in open spaces, which enables them to live alongside humans very well.

(18) Because of these characteristics, starlings can crowd out native bird species from their original homes. (19) Also, the size of their flocks can grow into the thousands. (20) Therefore, they can pose a great danger to crops. (21) Just imagine the damage that thousands of hungry birds can do to a field of just-planted seeds!

Duplicating any part of this book is prohibited by law.

25. Which of the following words from paragraph 1 is spelled correctly?

A. oregin

B. widespred

C. tonge

D. taught

26. Read sentence 5 from the passage.

Of course, about three centuries after he wrote this play, Shakespeare could not have predicted what would be done because of these lines.

Which is the BEST way to rewrite sentence 5?

A. Of course, Shakespeare, about three centuries after he wrote this play, could not have predicted what would be done because of these lines.

B. Of course, Shakespeare could not have predicted, about three centuries after he wrote this play, what would be done because of these lines.

C. Of course, Shakespeare could not have predicted what would be done, about three centuries after he wrote this play, because of these lines.

D. Of course, Shakespeare could not have predicted what would be done because of these lines about three centuries after he wrote this play.

27. Read sentence 8 from the passage.

The practice of bringing species from the Old World to the New World was commen at the time.

What is the correct way to spell commen?

A. comman

B. commin

C. common

D. commun

28. Read sentence 15 from the passage.

They can live in a variety of kinds of places.

Which is the BEST word to replace live in this sentence to show that starlings do well in a variety of kinds of places?

A. thrive

B. last

C. function

D. exist

Duplicating any part of this book is prohibited by law.

29. Read sentences 19 and 20 from the passage.

> **Also, the size of their flocks can grow into the thousands. Therefore, they can pose a great danger to crops.**

Which shows these sentences correctly combined into one complex sentence?

A. Also, the size of their flocks can grow into the thousands and pose a great danger to crops.

B. Also, the size of their flocks can grow into the thousands, they can pose a great danger to crops.

C. Also, because the size of their flocks can grow into the thousands, they can pose a great danger to crops.

D. Also, with the size of their flocks growing into the thousands, they can pose a great danger to crops.

30. Read sentence 16 from the passage.

> **Similarly, including seeds, fruits, and invertebrates, starlings can eat just about anything.**

Rewrite this sentence, placing the participial phrase <u>including seeds, fruits, and invertebrates</u> closer to the word it modifies.

_____

_____

_____

Duplicating any part of this book is prohibited by law.

Part 3: Writing

Persuasive Writing Prompt

Cigarette smoking leads to illnesses that are a huge drain on our health-care system. Most people agree that cigarettes should be heavily taxed. But obesity and diabetes are also major problems in the United States that seriously affect our health-care system. Write a persuasive essay that asserts whether or not soft drinks should be heavily taxed, as cigarettes are, to make them more expensive. Use reasons and examples to support your response.

Use the checklist below to help you do your best writing.

Does your essay

❏ clearly address the issue?

❏ introduce an opinion about the issue?

❏ support the opinion with logical reasoning and relevant, accurate evidence?

❏ acknowledge other opinions, including opinions that oppose your claim?

❏ organize reasons and evidence in a logical structure?

❏ use a variety of sentence lengths and styles?

❏ use a formal style and vocabulary suitable for the audience and purpose?

❏ provide an appropriate conclusion for the argument?

Use the following pages to plan and write your response.

Duplicating any part of this book is prohibited by law.

Planning Page

Duplicating any part of this book is prohibited by law.

Duplicating any part of this book is prohibited by law.

Duplicating any part of this book is prohibited by law.

Duplicating any part of this book is prohibited by law.

Duplicating any part of this book is prohibited by law.

Summative Assessment

Duplicating any part of this book is prohibited by law.

Part 1: Reading Comprehension

Read the passage and answer the questions that follow.

adapted from

The Necklace

by Guy de Maupassant

She was one of those pretty and charming girls with no dowry, no expectations, no means of being known, understood, loved, or married by a man rich and distinguished; and so she married a clerk in the Department of Education. She suffered intensely, feeling herself born for every delicacy and every luxury. She had no dresses, no jewelry, nothing. And she loved nothing else; she felt herself made for that only.

But one evening, her husband came in holding in his hand a large envelope. She quickly tore open the envelope and took out of it a printed card which bore these words: "The Minister of Education and Mrs. Georges Rampouneau beg Mr. and Mrs. Loisel to do them the honor to pass the evening with them at the palace of the Ministry, on Monday, January 18."

She threw the invitation on the table, murmuring, "What do you want me to do with that?"

"But, my dear, I thought you would be pleased. You will see there all <u>the official world</u>." He paused suddenly, seeing that his wife was weeping, and stuttered, "What's the matter?"

"Nothing. Only I have no clothes, and therefore I cannot go to this party."

"See here, Mathilde, how much would this cost, a proper dress, which would do on other occasions; something very simple?"

She answered hesitatingly, "I don't know exactly, but it seems to me that with four hundred francs I might do it."

He grew a little pale, but he said, "All right."

The day of the party drew near, and Mrs. Loisel seemed sad, restless, anxious. Yet, her dress was ready. One evening, her husband asked her, "What's the matter?"

"It annoys me not to have a jewel, not a single stone, to put on. I would almost rather not go to this party."

But her husband cried, "What a goose you are! Go find your friend, Mrs. Forester, and ask her to lend you some jewelry."

Mrs. Loisel gave a cry of joy. "That's true. I had not thought of it."

The next day, she went to her friend's and told her about her distress. Mrs. Forester went to her mirrored wardrobe, took out a large jewelry case, and said to Mrs. Loisel, "Choose, my dear."

All at once, Mrs. Loisel discovered, in a box of black satin, a superb necklace of diamonds. Her hands trembled in taking it up. She fastened it round her neck and asked, hesitating, full of anxiety, "Can you lend me this, only this?"

Duplicating any part of this book is prohibited by law.

"Yes, yes, certainly."

Mrs. Loisel sprang to her friend's neck, kissed her with ardor, and then escaped with her treasure.

The day of the party arrived. Mrs. Loisel was a success. She was the prettiest of them all, elegant, gracious, smiling, and mad with joy. All the men were looking at her, inquiring her name, asking to be introduced. She didn't leave the party until about four in the morning.

Upon returning home, however, she discovered that she no longer had the necklace around her neck! She turned to her husband, terror-stricken, "I—I—I do not have Mrs. Forester's diamond necklace!"

"What? How? It is not possible!"

They searched everywhere. They did not find it. They gazed at each other, crushed. At last, Mr. Loisel put on his overcoat again. "I'm going," he said, "back the whole distance we came on foot to see if I cannot find it."

He came back about seven o'clock. He had found nothing. Then he went to police headquarters, to the newspapers to offer a reward, to the cab company. At the end of a week, they had lost all hope. And Mr. Loisel, aged by five years, declared, "We must see how we can replace those jewels."

They went from jeweler to jeweler; both of them were sick with grief and anxiety. In a shop in the Palais Royal, they found a diamond necklace that seemed to them absolutely like the one they were seeking. It was priced 40,000 francs. They could have it for 36,000.

Mr. Loisel possessed 18,000 francs which his father had left him. He had to borrow the remainder. He borrowed, asking a thousand francs from one person, five hundred from another; and, frightened by all the anguish about the future, he went to buy the new diamond necklace.

When Mrs. Loisel took the newly acquired necklace to Mrs. Forester, the latter said, with an irritated air, "You ought to have brought it back sooner, for I might have needed it."

Mrs. Loisel learned the horrible life of the needy. She made the best of it, moreover, frankly, heroically. The frightful debt must be paid. She would pay it. Every month, they had to repay some of the loans and renew others to gain time. Mr. Loisel worked in the evening, doing bookkeeping for a shopkeeper.

At the end of ten years, they had paid everything back, everything. Mrs. Loisel seemed aged now. She had become the robust woman, hard and rough, of a poor household. But sometimes, when her husband was at the office, she sat down by the window and thought of that party, where she had been so beautiful and so admired. What would have happened if she had not lost that necklace?

Then, one Sunday, as she was taking a turn in the Champs Elysées, she suddenly noticed a woman walking with a child. It was Mrs. Forester, still young, still beautiful. Mrs. Loisel drew near.

"Good morning, Jeanne."

The other did not recognize her. She hesitated, "But—madam—I don't know—are you not making a mistake?"

Duplicating any part of this book is prohibited by law.

"No. I am Mathilde Loisel."

"Oh! My poor Mathilde, how you are changed."

"Yes, I have had hard days since I saw you. Do you remember that diamond necklace that you lent me to go to the party at the Ministry?"

"Yes?"

"Well, I lost it. I brought you back another just like it. And now, for ten years, we have been paying for it. At last, it is done, and I am mighty glad."

"You say that you bought a diamond necklace to replace mine?"

"Yes. You did not notice it, even, did you?" And she smiled with proud and naïve joy.

Mrs. Forester, much moved, took her by both hands. "Oh, my poor Mathilde. But my diamonds were false. At most, they were worth five hundred francs!"

Duplicating any part of this book is prohibited by law.

1. Mr. Loisel says that his wife will see "all the official world" at the party at the ministry. Which BEST describes what he means by the phrase the official world?

   A. the real world

   B. the offices at his workplace

   C. the world of those with power

   D. the world of luxury, grace, and beauty

2. Read these sentences from the passage.

   She answered hesitatingly, "I don't know exactly, but it seems to me that with four hundred francs I might do it." He grew a little pale, but he said, "All right."

   Based on Mr. Loisel's response to Mathilde Loisel's request for four hundred francs for a dress, which BEST describes his attitude toward his wife?

   A. She frightens him.

   B. He tries to make her happy.

   C. He resents her desire for luxuries.

   D. She inspires him to work harder.

3. How do Mrs. Forester's feelings about her jewelry differ from those of Mathilde Loisel?

   A. She is more casual about her jewelry.

   B. She is very excited about her jewelry.

   C. She is particularly jealous about her jewelry.

   D. She is extremely cautious about her jewelry.

4. How does Mathilde Loisel change after losing the necklace?

   A. She dreams day and night about being wealthy.

   B. She becomes willing and able to live in poverty.

   C. She becomes even more beautiful and admired.

   D. She regrets marrying a man with such a small income.

Duplicating any part of this book is prohibited by law.

5. What action could the Loisels have taken that would MOST LIKELY have resulted in a totally different outcome for them?

   A. Tell Mrs. Forester right after the party that the necklace was lost.

   B. Turn themselves in to the authorities right after the party.

   C. Replace the one that was lost with an even grander one.

   D. Work harder to pay their debts faster.

6. Based on what Mathilde Loisel learns at the end of the passage, what do you conclude is the theme of "The Necklace"?

   _____

   _____

   _____

   _____

   _____

Duplicating any part of this book is prohibited by law.

Read the poem and answer the questions that follow.

October in Tennessee
by Walter Malone

Far, far away, beyond a hazy height,
    The turquoise skies are hung in dreamy sleep;
Below, the fields of cotton, fleecy-white,
    Are spreading like a mighty flock of sheep.

5   Now, like Aladdin of the days of old,
    October robes the weeds in purple gowns;
He sprinkles all the sterile fields with gold,
    And all the rustic trees wear royal crowns.

The straggling fences all are interlaced
10   With pink and purple morning-glory blooms;
The starry asters glorify the <u>waste</u>,
    While grasses stand on guard with pikes and plumes.

Yet still amid the splendor of decay
    The chill winds call for blossoms that are dead,
15   The cricket chirps for sunshine passed away,—
    The lovely summer songsters that have fled.

And lonesome in a haunt of withered vines,
    Amid the flutter of her withered leaves,
Pale Summer for her perished kingdom pines,
20   And all the glories of her golden sheaves.

In vain October wooes her to remain
    Within the palace of his scarlet bowers,—
Entreats her to forget her heart-break pain,
    And weep no more above her faded flowers.

25   At last November, like a conqueror, comes
    To storm the golden city of his foe;
We hear his rude winds like the roll of drums,
    Bringing their desolation and their woe.

Duplicating any part of this book is prohibited by law.

The sunset, like a vast vermilion flood,
30   Splashes its giant glowing waves on high,
The forest flames with blazes red as blood,—
A conflagration sweeping to the sky.

Then all the treasures of that brilliant state
Are gathered in a mighty funeral pyre;
35 October, like a King resigned to fate,
Dies in his forests with their sunset fire.

Duplicating any part of this book is prohibited by law.

7. The imagery in lines 5–8 portrays the weeds, fields, and trees of October as

   A. magical.

   B. barren.

   C. aristocratic.

   D. ancient.

8. In line 11, the word <u>waste</u> connotes the idea of things that

   A. have been neglected.

   B. are completely useless.

   C. have been squandered.

   D. litter the landscape.

9. In lines 21–24, October is personified as a

   A. lover of Summer.

   B. careless heartbreaker.

   C. wealthy landowner.

   D. mother in mourning.

10. The imagery in lines 29–32 emphasizes the

   A. sensations that the speaker feels.

   B. sounds that the speaker hears.

   C. scents that the speaker smells.

   D. sights that the speaker sees.

Duplicating any part of this book is prohibited by law.

11. The mood at the end of the poem could BEST be described as

   A. triumphant.

   B. angry.

   C. sad.

   D. joyful.

12. A lyric poem is a short poem that shows the speaker's feelings or state of mind, often through the use of imagery. Explain why "October in Tennessee" could be described as a lyric poem.

   _____

   _____

   _____

   _____

   _____

Duplicating any part of this book is prohibited by law.

Read the passage and answer the questions that follow.

The Best Lunch Is a Local Lunch

The National School Lunch Program (NSLP) is a meal program for students that has been supported by the federal government for more than sixty years. The program has a broad reach, serving millions of students in more than 101,000 public schools, private schools, and childcare institutions. The main purpose of the program is to provide free or low-cost, nutritional lunches to students at these locations. Common policies and practices, however, are undermining this purpose. These policies and practices result in meals of doubtful nutritional value and are possibly also unnecessarily driving up costs. Fortunately, there is a movement underway to address the problem, with benefits to both farmers and children.

What's the Problem?

The NSLP supports school lunches in two ways. First, the United States Department of Agriculture (USDA), which runs the NSLP, provides a cash reimbursement for each meal served at participating schools. Second, participating schools can receive free food—called "entitlement" and "bonus" foods—directly from the USDA. Policies and practices related to this second form of support, however, are questionable.

As provided by the USDA, entitlement and bonus foods are mostly unprocessed, including such commodities as fresh apples, meat, and eggs. Schools may prepare this food themselves on site. Schools—or state distribution agencies—may also pay a private company to process the food. In processing the food, however, two things happen to it: It becomes less nutritious and more expensive. Chicken is processed into fried chicken nuggets, potatoes into French fries, apples and other fruits into pastries, and so on. These foods may be more convenient for schools, but they are also often loaded with additional sugar, fat, and salt. Furthermore, they are costly. For example, according to the *New York Times,* raw chicken provided to the Michigan Department of Education and valued at $11.40 a case is processed into nuggets that cost $33.45 a case.

Adding to the problem is that many schools and school districts do not run their lunch programs themselves, but instead hire private food service management companies to do so. Despite what they may claim, these companies do not typically work in the best interests either of children or even of the school districts that hired them. For example, such companies receive rebates for purchasing processed food and then serve the less healthful food to children without passing on the savings to school districts. These companies have also fought—and defeated—rules proposed by the USDA that would make school lunches healthier.

Duplicating any part of this book is prohibited by law.

Local Solutions to a National Problem

Led by grassroots organizations and popularized by such food writers as Michael Pollen, Barbara Kingsolver, and Mark Bittman, a grassroots movement has been growing in recent years both in the United States and abroad, calling attention to the environmental and health costs of our increasing reliance on processed foods. The proposed solutions are simple: Bring food production and preparation back home, or close to home. Start your own garden, for example, or, if you can't, support small local farms by purchasing food through Community Supported Agriculture programs (CSAs) and farmers' markets. And, most importantly, prepare more of your meals in your own kitchen.

These ideas are making their way to school lunch programs. The USDA's Farm to School initiative, for example, strives to get more healthy, locally produced food into school meals by connecting schools with the small farms in their area. Other remarkable programs are springing up as the result of local efforts. Consider the program at the Village School, a public charter school in Eugene, Oregon. When the school district decided to reduce food service to public charter schools, local parents Toña Aguilar and Stacey Black wrote a proposal for a new meal plan at their children's school. Their plan called for purchasing as much organic and local food as possible and cooking all meals on site. The results? Not only are the locally produced and prepared meals more healthful, but they are also more popular. Within a month, the school was selling twice as many meals as before. The salad bar—serving fresh, local produce—is especially popular. Yes, when fruits and vegetables are prepared well, kids really do like them!

Duplicating any part of this book is prohibited by law.

13. Which text structure is used in this passage?

A. cause and effect

B. problem and solution

C. compare and contrast

D. chronological order

14. Read this sentence from the passage.

Chicken is processed into fried chicken nuggets, potatoes into French fries, apples and other fruits into pastries, and so on.

The examples in this sentence are given in order to show that processed food is

A. less healthy.

B. tastier.

C. more varied.

D. worth the cost.

15. Which word or phrase in paragraph 6 BEST shows the author's attitude toward efforts to make school lunch programs healthier?

A. strives

B. locally produced

C. remarkable

D. springing up

16. Why is the grassroots movement that has been calling attention to the costs of processed foods relevant to this passage?

A. The movement is influencing school lunch programs.

B. The movement supports private management of school lunch programs.

C. The movement has been popularized by many well-known writers.

D. The movement is interested in environmental problems related to processed foods.

Duplicating any part of this book is prohibited by law.

17. Although the presentation of information in this passage is objective, the author seems to be biased against

A. school lunches.

B. the USDA.

C. food service management companies.

D. small farmers.

18. In 2–3 sentences, summarize the ways in which school lunches could be made more healthy, according to this passage.

_____

_____

_____

_____

_____

Duplicating any part of this book is prohibited by law.

Read the passage and answer the questions that follow.

Let Them Grow Their Own Food!

Will absurdity never end? In January 2011, the United States Department of Agriculture (USDA) proposed changes to its rules for its National School Lunch Program (NSLP). These rule changes included such sensible proposals as cutting back on starchy vegetables, such as potatoes, in favor of other vegetables, not counting the tomato sauce on pizza as a vegetable, and gradually reducing the amount of sodium allowed in school meals. And what happened? The food industry lobbied hard, and by November, Congress caved in. Thanks to our fine representatives, when it comes to school lunches, what passes as nutritious is in reality anything but. And yes, folks: in school cafeterias across our nation, pizza is still considered a vegetable.

The time has come for us to take a hard look at ourselves and ask the question, Is this really what we want for the children in our district? I say that it is not. I say that our children deserve better. I say: Let them grow their own food!

Have children grow their own food? To some, my proposal might sound like a punishment. However, there are many benefits to school garden programs, including the simple fact that they get children out of the classroom. Where's the punishment in that? Not only is it simply a delight to spend time digging in the dirt and helping things grow, but spending such time outdoors connects children to the natural world and encourages them to take care of their environment. School gardens also provide the opportunity for hands-on learning in just about every subject, particularly science, in which American students have proven to be weak. Furthermore, through gardening, children tend to open up to trying new, more healthful foods.

OK, you might say, all of these arguments are fine and good—but where exactly are our city kids going to find gardens to tend? After all, most of our schoolyards are paved over and used as playgrounds. True enough—so why not build gardens on the rooftops of our schools?

The idea is not as crazy as you might think. In fact, three schools in New York City—P.S. 64, the Tompkins Square Middle School, and the Earth School in Greenwich Village—are already jointly developing their own rooftop garden, which they call the Fifth Street Farm Project. The idea began with the organic container garden that Earth School teacher Abbe Futterman started with her students in order to teach them about health, nutrition, and organic farming. The garden has provided the school cafeteria with fruits, such as apples, figs, blueberries, and strawberries; vegetables, such as carrots, radishes, chard, broccoli, and more; and a variety of herbs. Just think how much more the rooftop garden will provide compared to the usual school lunch!

Duplicating any part of this book is prohibited by law.

Building a rooftop garden is not inexpensive. Therefore, I propose starting with just one garden, on the rooftop of our middle school. Starting small gives us a way to keep start-up costs down as well as to judge how effective the program is. I should point out, too, that green roofs do have financial benefits. They save energy by providing insulation, which results in lower heating and cooling costs. Also, tax abatements are available for green roofs. And, of course, the rooftop garden will be providing fruits, vegetables, and herbs for our cafeterias, benefiting our school meal programs in terms not only of the budget but also of health.

I will be submitting a formal proposal at the city council meeting next Tuesday. I urge you to come to the meeting or to call your councilperson in support of this project. Let's say "No!" to absurdity and "Yes!" to using our local resources to do right for our children.

Duplicating any part of this book is prohibited by law.

19. Which is the MAIN reason why the author supports rooftop gardens?

 A. They are cost effective.

 B. They save energy.

 C. They are organic.

 D. They can provide good food.

20. Which statement from the passage BEST reveals the author's bias?

 A. "Will absurdity never end?"

 B. "The food industry lobbied hard ..."

 C. "... pizza is still considered a vegetable."

 D "Have children grow their own food?"

21. The author devotes an entire paragraph to describing the Fifth Street Farm Project in order to show that rooftop gardens are

 A. reasonable.

 B. crazy.

 C. fashionable.

 D. expensive.

22. What persuasive technique does the author use throughout the passage?

 A. name-calling of those who would object to rooftop gardens

 B. responding to anticipated criticism

 C. using loaded words and phrases

 D. including testimonials of those in favor of rooftop gardens

Duplicating any part of this book is prohibited by law.

23. The authors of "The Best Lunch Is a Local Lunch" and "Let Them Grow Their Own Food!" agree that

    A. rooftop gardens are the best way to provide food for cafeterias.

    B. national policies about school lunch programs are a problem.

    C. private food service management companies are responsible for bad lunches.

    D. local efforts to provide good school lunches are not supported by the federal government.

24. What are the similarities between the methods for improving school lunches that are proposed in "The Best Lunch Is a Local Lunch" and "Let Them Grow Their Own Food!"?

_____

_____

_____

_____

_____

Duplicating any part of this book is prohibited by law.

Part 2: Language Arts

This passage contains mistakes. Read the passage and answer the questions that follow.

Extreme Endurance

(1) The marathon and triathlon are two of the best-known long-distance endurance events. (2) Thousands of people compete in these events every year, training for months to prepare for the day of the race. (3) In a marathon, competitors run 26.2 miles. (4) In a standard triathlon, competitors swim 500 meters, bike 40 kilometers, and run 10 kilometers. (5) It takes <u>elite</u> athletes more than two hours to complete either race, while ordinary athletes can take several hours to get to the finish line. (6) Would you believe, however, that there are even more challenging races than these for athletes to compete in?

(7) Competing in a race longer than the marathon is called *ultrarunning*, and the races themselves are often called *ultramarathons*. (8) There are many types of ultramarathons. (9) Some are defined by their length in distance: 50 kilometers, 100 kilometers, 50 miles, 100 miles, and 52.4 miles (a double marathon). (10) Others are defined by their length in time; six, twelve, and twenty-four hours are popular lengths. (11) The winner is the person who runs in a timed event the farthest within the given time.

(12) The most extreme of all ultramarathons is probably the Badwater Ultramarathon. (13) This race is 135 miles long and is run in the heat of mid-July. (14) The race begins in Death Valley, California, at 280 feet below sea level, the lowest elevation in the Western Hemisphere. (15) It ends at the <u>trailhead</u> for Mount Whitney, California, nearly 8,300 feet above sea level. (16) Some runners continue past the end of the official course and to the peak of Mount Whitney, which is the highest point in the contiguous United States. (17) Runners compete by invitation only, and only about ninety runners compete each year. (18) The current course records are just under twenty-three hours for men and just over twenty-six hours for women.

(19) The most extreme triathlon is called the Ironman Triathlon, in which competitors swim 2.4 miles, bike 112 miles, and run a complete marathon. (20) This event got its start in 1978 in Honolulu, Hawaii, when triathlete John Collins had the vision of combining the Waikiki Rough Water Swim, Around Oahu Bike Race, and Honolulu Marathon. (21) Ironman triathlons are now held all over the world, although the Hawaiian race, now held in Kona, remains the most famous. (22) Elite athletes complete the race in about eight or nine hours.

Duplicating any part of this book is prohibited by law.

25. Read sentence 1 from the passage.

> **The marathon and triathlon are two of the best-known long-distance endurance events.**

Which word in sentence 1 is LEAST necessary and should be deleted?

A. triathlon

B. best-known

C. endurance

D. events

26. Read sentence 5 from the passage.

> **It takes elite athletes more than two hours to complete either race, while ordinary athletes can take several hours to get to the finish line.**

Using the relationship between the terms "elite athletes" and "ordinary athletes," you can conclude that the word elite means

A. poor.

B. normal.

C. trained.

D. best.

27. Read sentence 11 from the passage.

> **The winner is the person who runs in a timed event the farthest within the given time.**

What is the BEST way to rewrite sentence 11?

A. In a timed event, the winner is the person who runs the farthest within the given time.

B. The winner is the person in a timed event who runs the farthest within the given time.

C. The winner is the person who runs the farthest in a timed event within the given time.

D. The winner is the person who runs the farthest, within the given time in a timed event.

28. Read this entry from a glossary.

> **trailhead**   start of a trail

Which word is closest in meaning to that of trailhead?

A. beginning

B. path

C. summit

D. conclusion

Duplicating any part of this book is prohibited by law.

29. Read sentence 16 from the passage.

> **Some runners continue past the end of the official course and to the peak of Mount Whitney, which is the highest point in the contiguous United States.**

In sentence 16, the prepositional phrase <u>to the peak of Mount Whitney</u> modifies which word?

A. runners

B. continue

C. official

D. point

30. Read sentences 12 and 13 from the passage.

> **The most extreme of all ultramarathons is probably the Badwater Ultramarathon. This race is 135 miles long and is run in the heat of mid-July.**

Combine these sentences into one, using the relative pronoun *which* to create a subordinate clause.

_____

_____

_____

_____

_____

Duplicating any part of this book is prohibited by law.

Part 3: Writing

Read the passages and respond to the prompt that follows.

Marine Debris: A Definition

According to the National Oceanic and Atmospheric Administration (NOAA), marine debris is "any persistent solid material that is manufactured or processed and directly or indirectly, intentionally or unintentionally, disposed of or abandoned into the marine environment or the Great Lakes." In other words, this debris is composed of solid (rather than gas or fluid), long-lasting, human-made materials that have, in one way or another, made it into the sea. Most marine debris is plastic waste. Besides creating an eyesore, it causes a number of problems. It damages marine habitats, such as coral reefs. It harms animals that become entangled in the debris. Even worse, animals may mistake the debris for food or simply eat it by accident, which can lead to internal injury, starvation, or death.

The Great Pacific Garbage Patch is probably the best-known and most concentrated area of marine debris. The name, however, is misleading. It conjures up a picture of an island of litter, floating like an enormous blanket on the surface of the ocean. This picture is inaccurate. Although the garbage patch does include large items, such as fishing nets, most of the debris is composed of small pieces of plastic. Also, much of this plastic floats not at the surface, but as far as three hundred feet below the surface.

Marine debris is an eyesore, and even worse.

Duplicating any part of this book is prohibited by law.

Cleaning Up the Garbage Patch
from the NOAA Marine Debris Program

Is debris cleanup feasible in the "garbage patches" and other areas of our oceans?

The answer to this is not as simple as you may think. It is certainly not cost-effective to skim the surface of the entire ocean. Even a cleanup focusing on "garbage patches" would be a tremendous challenge. Keep in mind these points:

- Concentration areas move and change throughout the year
- These areas are typically very large (see below)
- The marine debris is not distributed evenly within these areas
- Modes of transport and cleanup will likely require fuel of some sort
- Most of the marine debris found in these areas is small bits of plastic

This all adds up to a bigger challenge than even sifting beach sand to remove bits of marine debris. **In some areas where marine debris concentrates, so does marine life.** This makes simply skimming the debris risky—more harm than good may be caused. Remember that much of our ocean life is in the microscopic size range. For example, straining ocean waters for plastics (e.g., microplastics) would capture the plankton that are the base of the marine food web and responsible for 50 percent of the photosynthesis on Earth ... roughly equivalent to all land plants!

Also, keep in mind that our oceans are immense areas! The Pacific Ocean is the largest ocean on the planet, covering nearly 30 percent of Earth's surface (about 96 million square miles). Surveying less than 1 percent of the North Pacific Ocean, a three-degree swath between 30 and 35°N and 150 and 180°W, requires covering a massive area. If you traveled at twenty kilometers an hour for ten hours a day, and surveyed an area within one hundred meters off of each side of your ship, it would take sixty-eight ships one year to cover that area! Now, add to that the fact that these areas of debris concentration have no distinct boundaries, move throughout the year, and are affected by seasons, climate, El Niño, etc.

Reduce or Recycle?

Longtime marine researcher Charles Moore believes that, given our current knowledge and technology, cleaning up the Great Pacific Garbage Patch is an impossible task. He believes that the best way to reduce marine debris is to reduce our use of plastic. However, the production and use of plastic has actually been growing rapidly—doubling from 60 billion pounds in 1987 to 120 billion pounds in 2007—and continues to grow. Keith Cristman of the American Chemistry Council, which represents the interests of plastic manufacturers, disagrees with Moore about reducing the use of plastic. "Plastic is a valuable resource," he says. "It shouldn't be wasted; it should be recycled."

Duplicating any part of this book is prohibited by law.

Informative/Explanatory Writing Prompt

In your own words, explain what the Great Pacific Garbage Patch is, its potential consequences, and the difficulties associated with any attempt to clean it up. Support your response with details from the resources provided.

Use the checklist below to help you do your best writing.

Does your informative essay

❑ introduce a topic clearly?

❑ use facts, definitions, details, quotations, and examples to develop the topic?

❑ quote and credit sources accurately?

❑ organize ideas and information in a way that makes sense?

❑ use vivid and exact words, including appropriate technical vocabulary?

❑ use transitional words and phrases to link your ideas?

❑ use a formal style and vocabulary that is suitable for the audience and purpose?

❑ have a conclusion that sums up your ideas?

❑ use correct spelling and use conventional grammar and mechanics?

Use the following pages to plan and write your response.

Duplicating any part of this book is prohibited by law

Planning Page

Duplicating any part of this book is prohibited by law.

Duplicating any part of this book is prohibited by law.

Duplicating any part of this book is prohibited by law.

Duplicating any part of this book is prohibited by law.

Duplicating any part of this book is prohibited by law.

Notes

Notes

Notes